lonely planet kids

THE CITIES ACTIVITY BOOK

Illustrated by
Livi Gosling and Tom Woolley

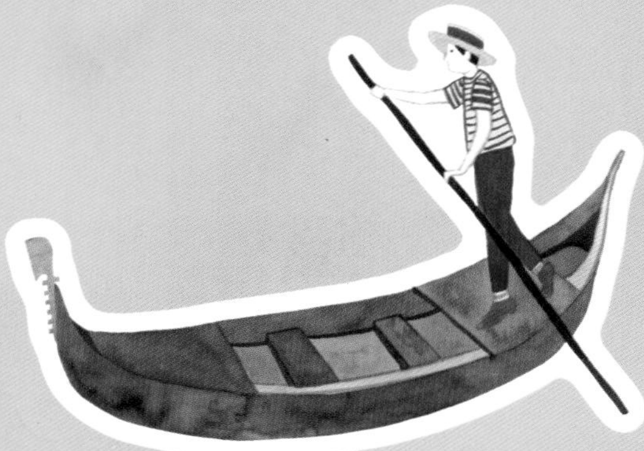

CONTENTS

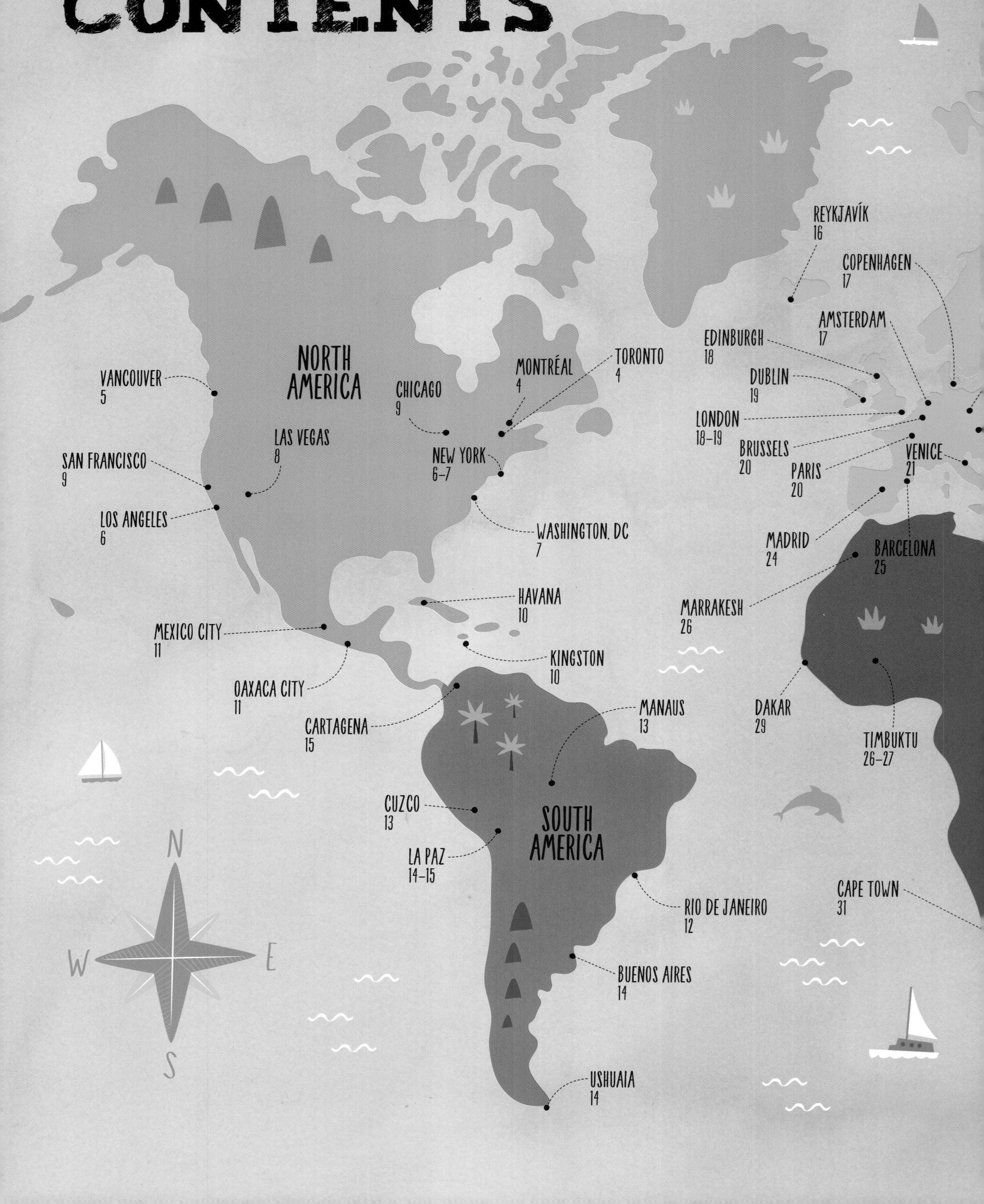

VANCOUVER 5
SAN FRANCISCO 9
LAS VEGAS 8
LOS ANGELES 6
CHICAGO 9
MONTRÉAL 4
TORONTO 4
NEW YORK 6–7
WASHINGTON, DC 7
HAVANA 10
MEXICO CITY 11
KINGSTON 10
OAXACA CITY 11
CARTAGENA 15
MANAUS 13
CUZCO 13
LA PAZ 14–15
RIO DE JANEIRO 12
BUENOS AIRES 14
USHUAIA 14
REYKJAVÍK 16
COPENHAGEN 17
AMSTERDAM 17
EDINBURGH 18
DUBLIN 19
LONDON 18–19
BRUSSELS 20
PARIS 20
VENICE 21
MADRID 24
BARCELONA 25
MARRAKESH 26
DAKAR 29
TIMBUKTU 26–27
CAPE TOWN 31

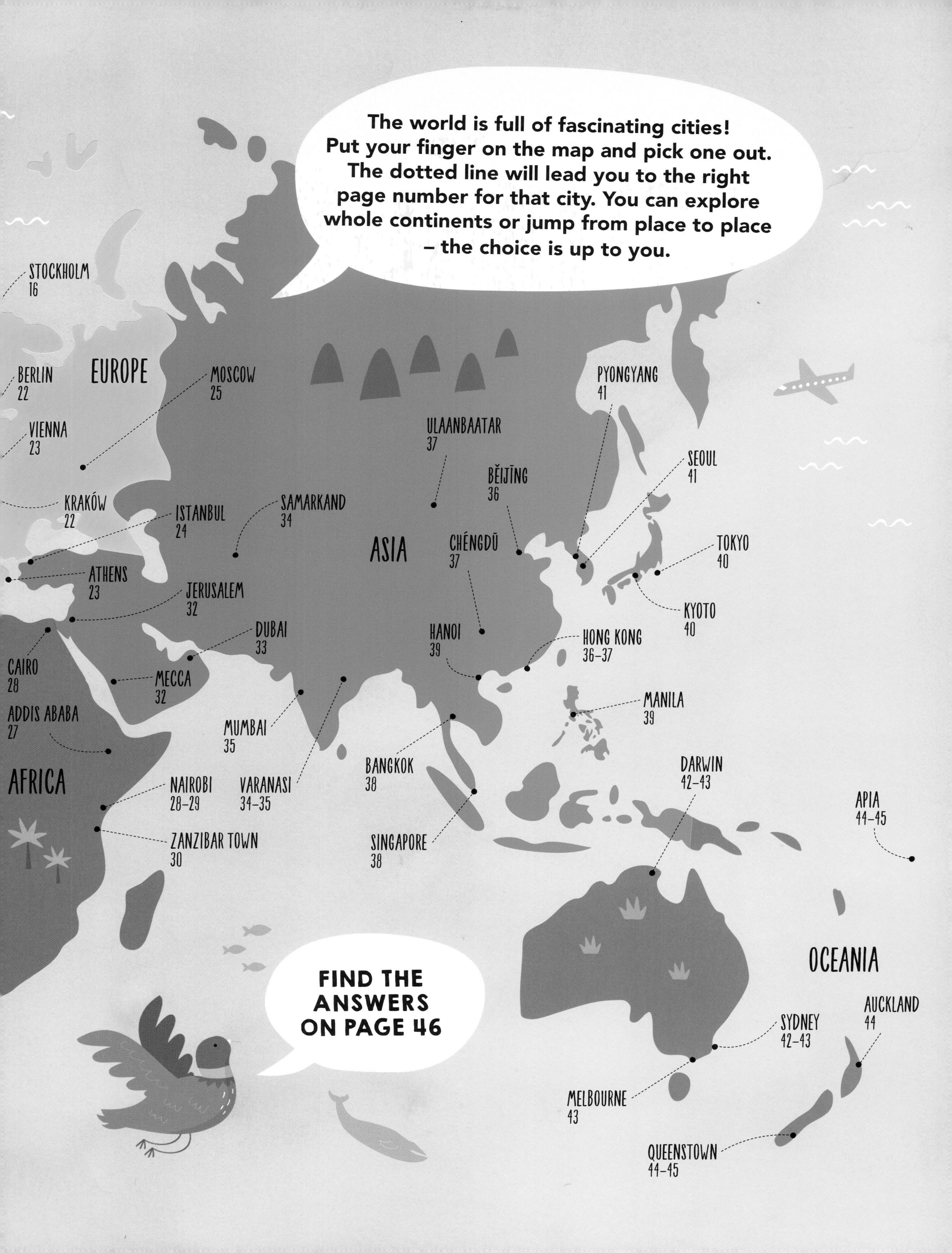
The world is full of fascinating cities! Put your finger on the map and pick one out. The dotted line will lead you to the right page number for that city. You can explore whole continents or jump from place to place – the choice is up to you.
STOCKHOLM 16
EUROPE
BERLIN 22
MOSCOW 25
VIENNA 23
KRAKÓW 22
ISTANBUL 24
ATHENS 23
JERUSALEM 32
SAMARKAND 34
CAIRO 28
DUBAI 33
MECCA 32
ADDIS ABABA 27
MUMBAI 35
AFRICA
NAIROBI 28–29
VARANASI 34–35
ZANZIBAR TOWN 30
ASIA
PYONGYANG 41
ULAANBAATAR 37
BĚIJĪNG 36
SEOUL 41
CHÉNGDŪ 37
TOKYO 40
KYOTO 40
HANOI 39
HONG KONG 36–37
MANILA 39
BANGKOK 38
SINGAPORE 38
DARWIN 42–43
APIA 44–45
OCEANIA
FIND THE ANSWERS ON PAGE 46
AUCKLAND 44
SYDNEY 42–43
MELBOURNE 43
QUEENSTOWN 44–45

MONTRÉAL

CANADA North America

Montréal is very French – residents say *bonjour* more often than 'hello'. It's a sociable metropolis that bustles with people playing in parks, gathering at festivals and meeting in outdoor cafés.

SPOT THE DIFFERENCE!
The city's Insectarium is famous for hosting insect-tasting events and serving up worm-topped pizza. Can you spot five differences between these delicious meals?

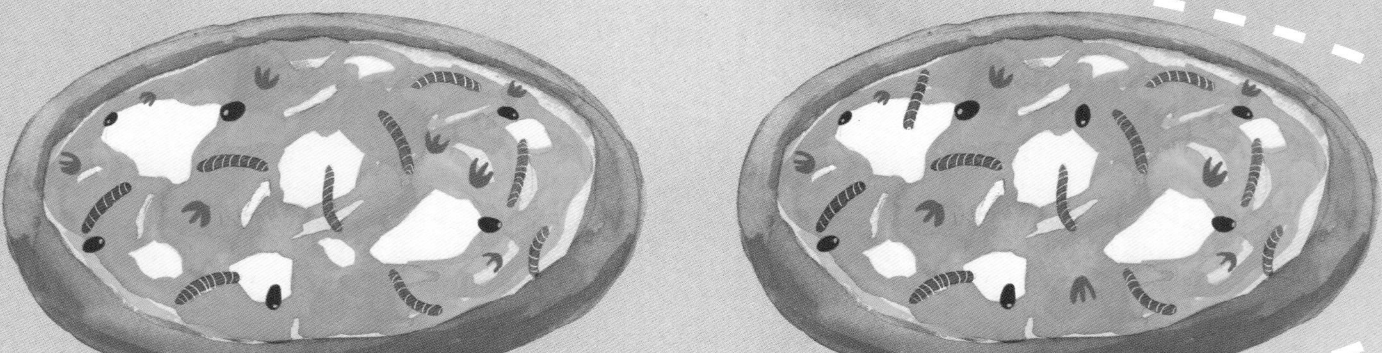

TORONTO

CANADA North America

With a population of more than six million, Toronto is far and away Canada's largest city. Everything's cool about this growing metropolis – from the icy winters to the silvery skyscrapers and the location on shimmering Lake Ontario.

HOW MANY ISLANDS?
The Toronto Islands lie in Lake Ontario. Cars aren't allowed there, so people bike and boat around. How many islands can you count in this picture?

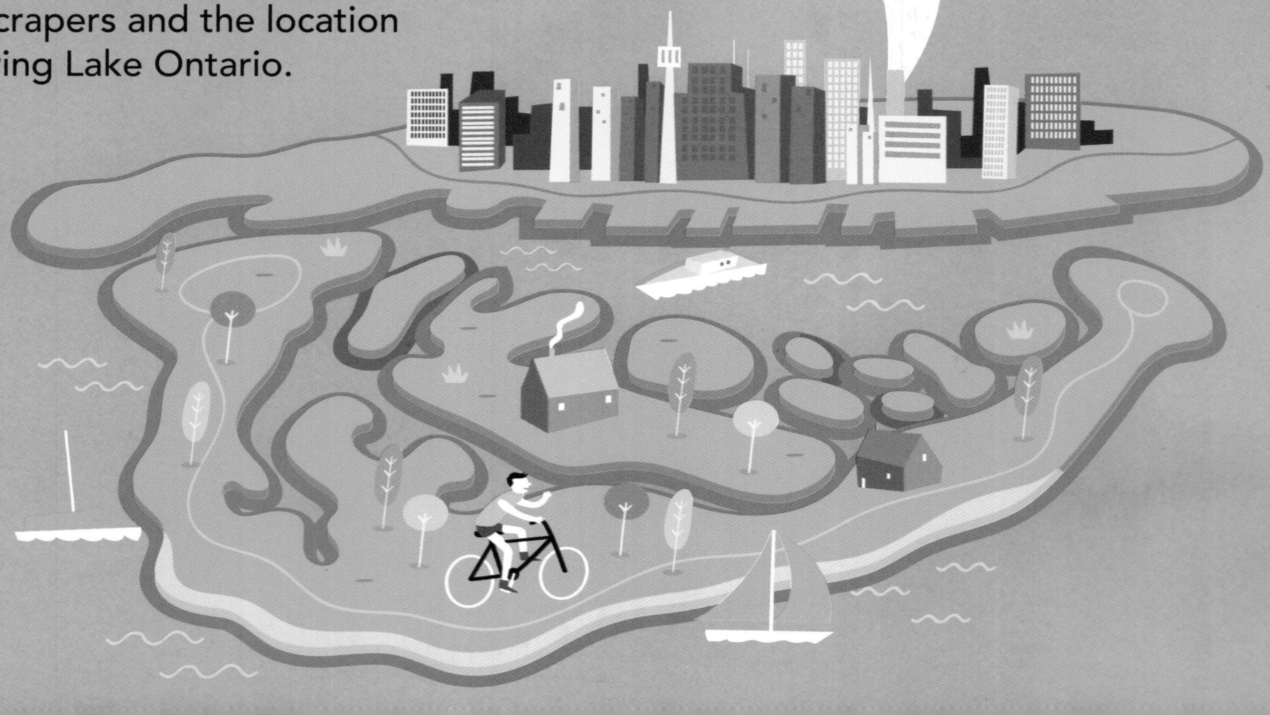

VANCOUVER

CANADA North America

Many people believe that Vancouver is the prettiest city on the planet, and who's to argue? The city sits where the mountains meet the sea and a rainforest grows from the edge of downtown. The people here are outdoorsy and laid-back, with a taste for adventurous eating.

COLOUR IN THE TOTEM POLE!

The native people of Canada have been making totem poles for centuries. Each one tells a story – colour in this one!

NEW YORK

USA North America

The world's most famous city is big, bold and impressive. Yellow cabs honk their way down busy streets, and steam used to heat buildings spurts from holes in the ground as New Yorkers jostle along the sidewalks.

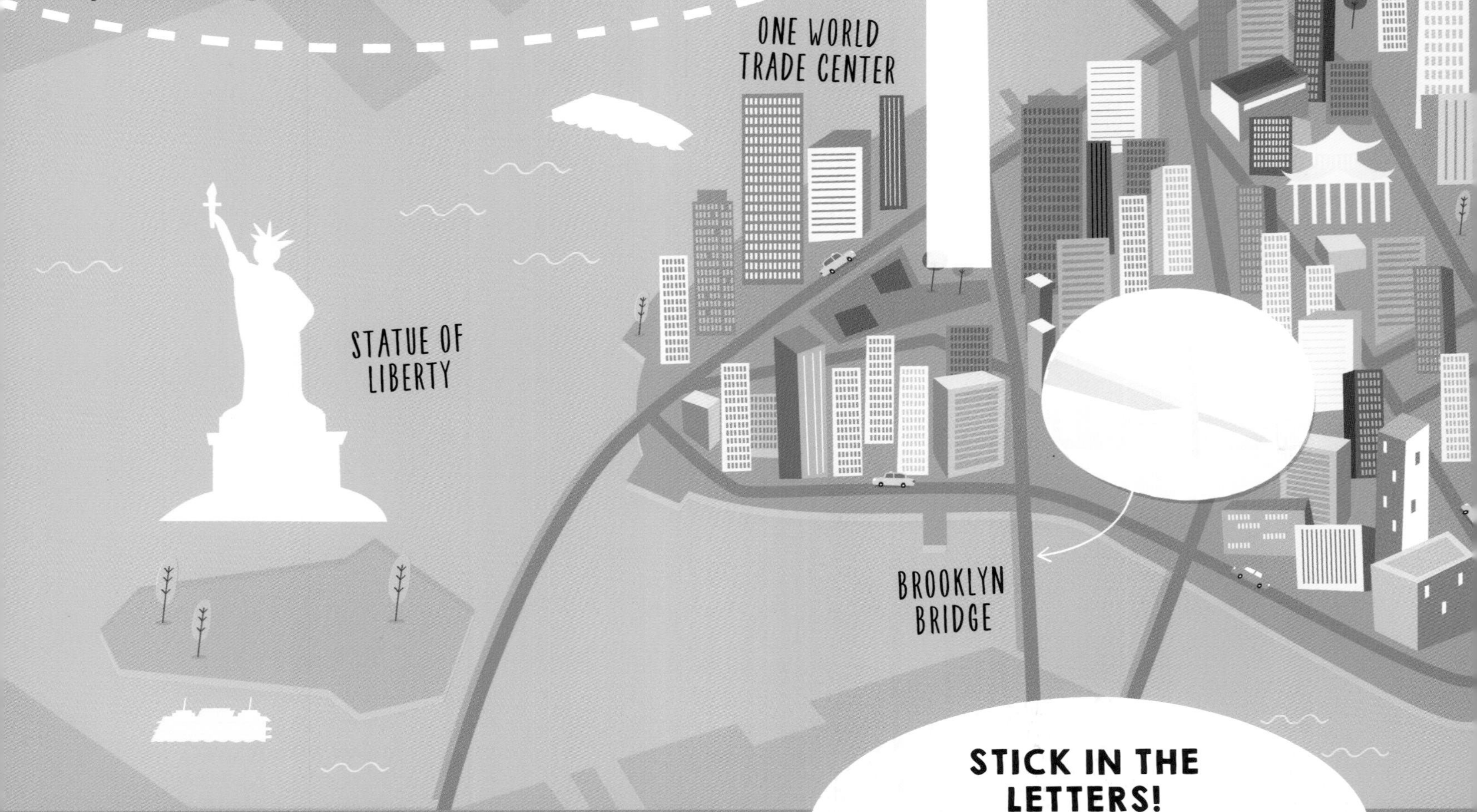

LOS ANGELES

USA North America

With golden beaches and virtually non-stop sunshine, Los Angeles is just as good-looking as its rich and famous residents. As the birthplace of blockbuster movies, the city is packed with reminders of the glittery world of show business.

STICK IN THE LETTERS!

Giant white letters spell out the word 'Hollywood' on a hillside overlooking the city. Find the letter stickers and stick in the word 'Hollywood' here!

WASHINGTON, DC

USA North America

New York may be the USA's Big Apple, but Washington, DC is the country's capital. It's a place of grand ministerial buildings, including the domed Capitol and the White House. The streets also buzz with busy students and crowds of excited tourists.

COUNT THE WINDOWS!
The home of the president is known as the White House. How many windows can you count?

LAS VEGAS

USA North America

Rising from the desert like a neon oasis, Las Vegas is a jaw-dropping extravaganza. At the heart of the city is Las Vegas Boulevard (often called 'the Strip'), a stretch of road where you can find some of the world's biggest hotels. These try to lure people in with their colossal casinos and wacky themes. In this crazy, colourful city you can find a half-size Eiffel Tower and experience thrills and spills riding a roller coaster at the top of the Stratosphere hotel.

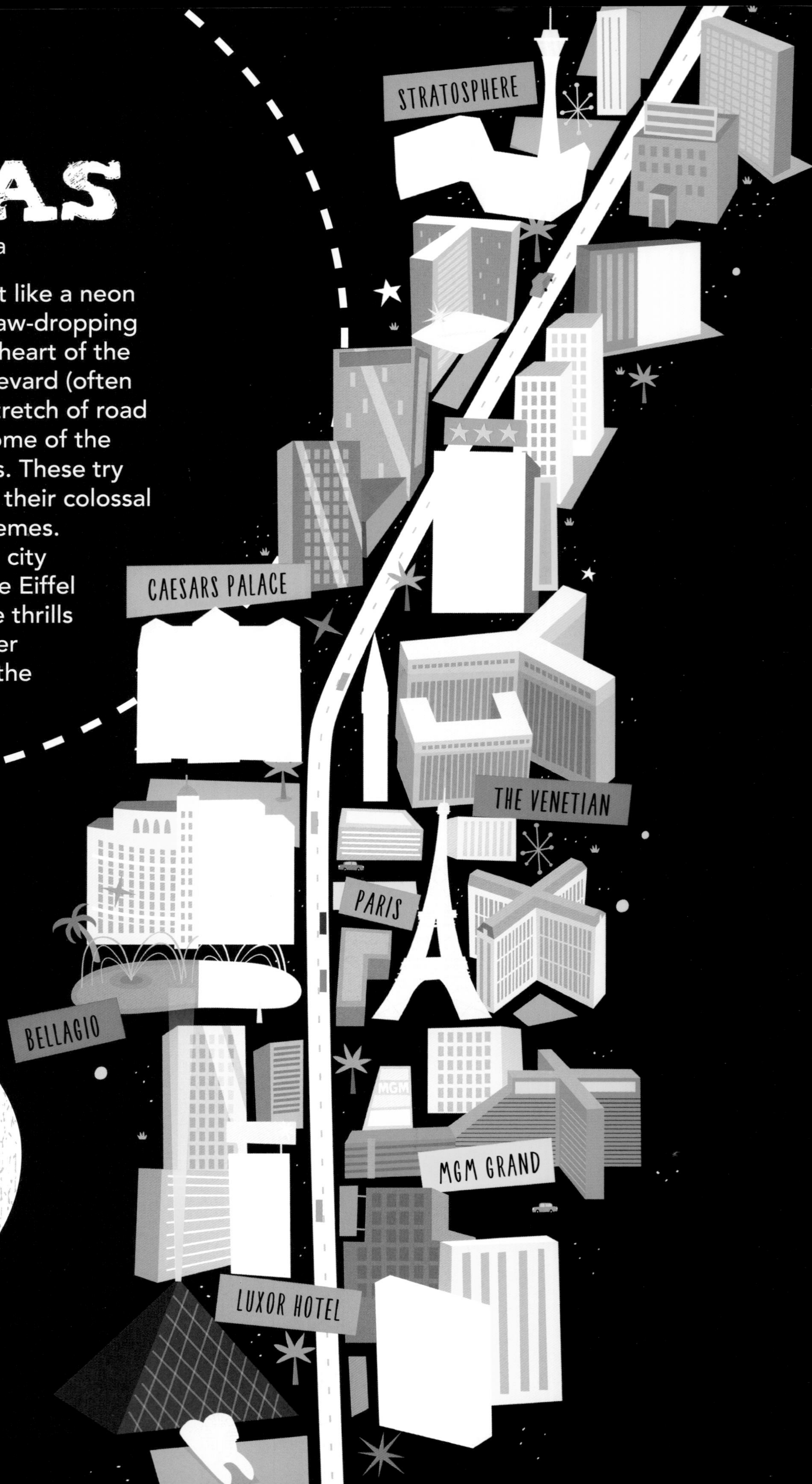

USE STICKERS TO FILL IN THE SIGHTS!

Get your stickers and fill in some of the amazing hotels and sights that make up the Strip!

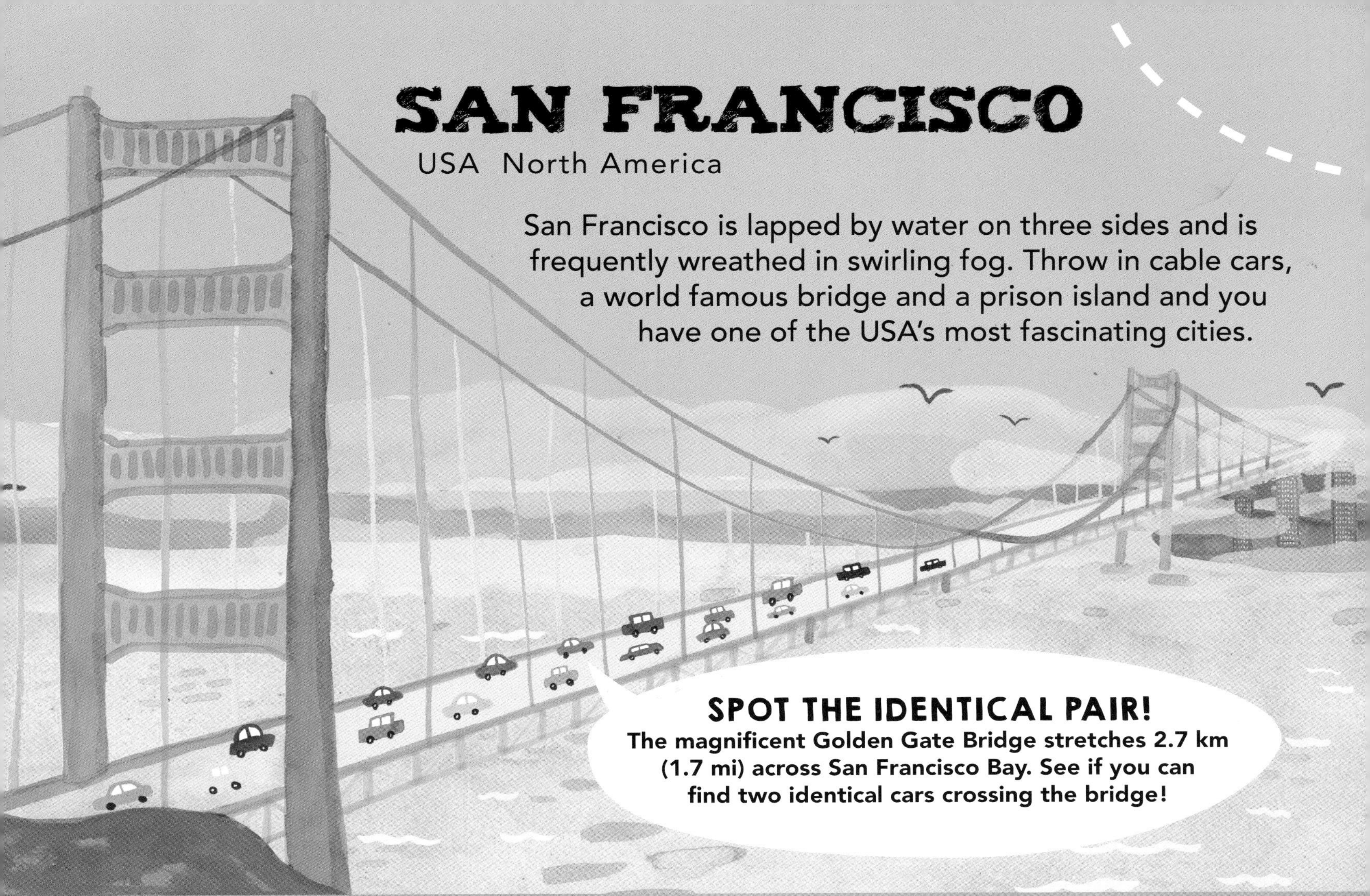

SAN FRANCISCO

USA North America

San Francisco is lapped by water on three sides and is frequently wreathed in swirling fog. Throw in cable cars, a world famous bridge and a prison island and you have one of the USA's most fascinating cities.

SPOT THE IDENTICAL PAIR!

The magnificent Golden Gate Bridge stretches 2.7 km (1.7 mi) across San Francisco Bay. See if you can find two identical cars crossing the bridge!

CHICAGO

USA North America

Chicago is tall – some of the world's mightiest skyscrapers rise up here. It's also beach-y, museum-y and inventive, with a backward-flowing river and trains that run on stilts.

DRAW IN FACES AND ADD STICKERS!

Trains clatter along tracks above the city. Draw in faces in the train windows and add stickers to complete the picture!

HAVANA

CUBA North America

Cuba is unlike anywhere else on Earth. In the capital, Havana, visitors feel like they've taken a time machine back to the 1950s. Vintage cars chug along the streets, while salsa dancing and dominoes are some of the favourite ways to have fun.

CAN YOU SPOT?

Colourful old buildings line Havana's busy streets. Can you spot the following in the picture? Add a smiley sticker for each one!

- A RED CAR
- RED CIRCLE TRAFFIC SIGN
- A THREE-WHEEL TAXI
- TWO YELLOW SHOP SIGNS
- A MAN WEARING A RED CAP
- A LIGHT ABOVE A DOOR
- TWO CARDBOARD BOXES
- A WHITE CAR WITH A BLACK ROOF

KINGSTON

JAMAICA North America

Kingston may be a small city on a small island, but it has made a big impact on the world. The city is famous for its cool, laidback style and toe-tapping reggae music, as well as being home to some of the fastest athletes on the planet.

WHAT DO YOU SAY?

People speak a unique dialect in Kingston and might say '*Wah gwan?*' (What's going on?) when they greet each other. Add the stickers and write in what you might say!

OAXACA CITY

MEXICO North America

The city of Oaxaca (pronounced 'waa-hah-kah') in southern Mexico is rich in history and traditions. It also is one of the most popular spots for celebrating the Day of the Dead festival, an annual event to honour the departed.

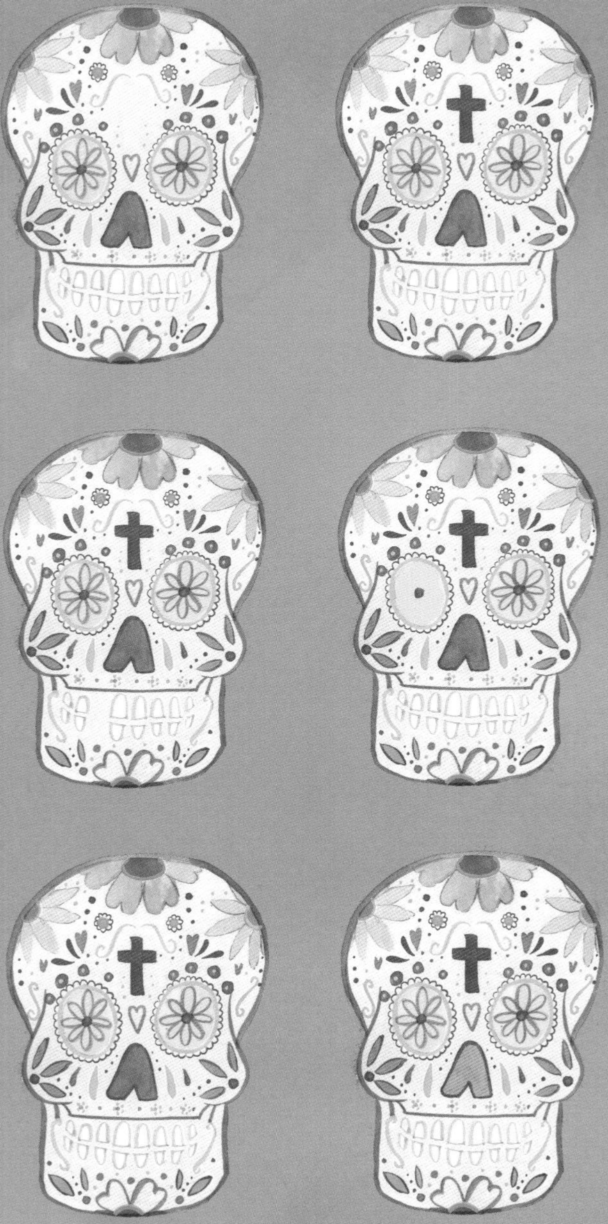

FIND THE IDENTICAL PAIR!
Skeletons can be found everywhere during the Day of the Dead festival. Which two skulls are identical?

MEXICO CITY

MEXICO North America

Mexico City is full of surprises. It is a place where you can buy voodoo dolls at the market or eat insects for dinner. It is also famously busy, with 20 million inhabitants all eating, sleeping and working side by side.

DESIGN A MASK!
Masked wrestling, known as *lucha libre*, is a popular Mexican sport, famed for its colourful costumes. Colour in and design your own fearsome mask!

RIO DE JANEIRO

BRAZIL South America

Each year, Rio explodes into a huge open-air party and everyone is invited! Carnival takes place in February or March during the lead-up to Lent. Rio's five-day celebration is the largest in the world, attracting two million revellers to the city streets every single day.

ADD STICKERS TO COMPLETE THE COSTUMES!
Find the stickers to complete these colourful samba school parade costumes!

MANAUS

BRAZIL South America

Manaus is located in the heart of the Amazon rainforest, home to one of the most varied populations of wildlife on the planet. The city is also a thriving metropolis with busy urban streets and an opera house.

COUNT THE SPIDER LEGS!

The rainforest around Manaus is crawling with creatures, including spiders! How many spider legs can you count in this picture?

CUZCO

PERU South America

Cuzco was once the capital of the great Inca empire and was later colonized by the Spanish. Here, you can see the locals leading llamas up the cobblestone streets. Fine boutiques and hotels cater for the tourists heading to the mountain-top ruins of the Inca city of Machu Picchu.

SPOT THE DIFFERENCE!

Can you spot six differences between these pictures of llamas and their owners?

BUENOS AIRES

ARGENTINA
South America

Buenos Aires moves to the rhythm of the tango. It's a city famous for its passion – for friends and family, music, the fine arts and of course, fútbol (football).

COLOUR IN!
Grab your pens or pencils and colour in this tango-dancing couple!

LA PAZ

BOLIVIA
South America

Take a deep breath – the air is thin in the high-altitude city of La Paz. Bolivia's capital sits in a valley, surrounded by the peaks of the Andes mountains. It was once the home of the Inca and Aymara peoples. Today skyscrapers rise up in the canyon and urban cable cars sway overhead.

USHUAIA

ARGENTINA South America

Remote and snow-covered, Ushuaia is the capital of a chain of islands called Tierra del Fuego, which means 'land of fire'. Despite Ushuaia's faraway feel, the city is expanding fast and streets dot the slopes of the Andes.

FIND THE IDENTICAL PAIR!
For thousands of years, Ushuaia was home to nomadic tribes. Can you find two identical tribesmen?

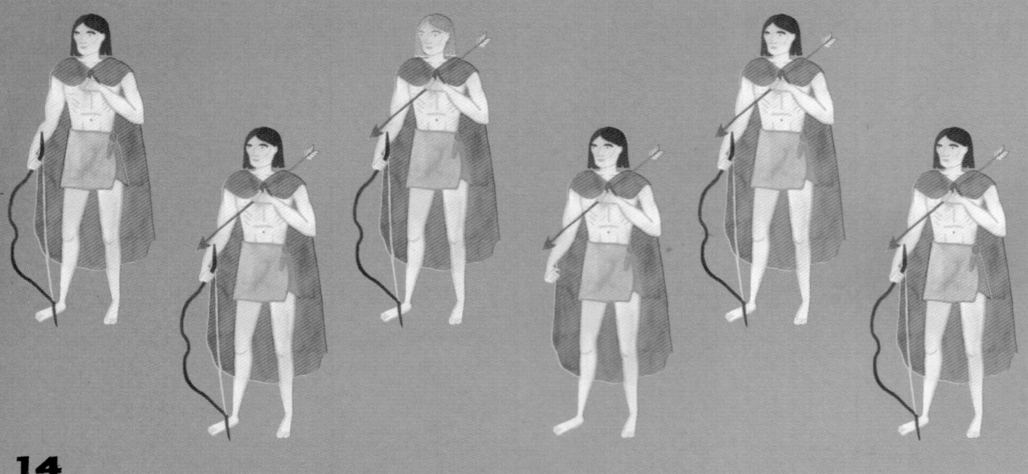

DRAW IN PASSENGERS!
La Paz has the largest urban cable-car system in the world. Find some pencils and draw in some passengers!

CARTAGENA

COLOMBIA South America

ADD STICKERS!
Find the stickers of the pirate ship, gold coins and glittering gilded objects, and stick them in here!

Cartagena de Indias is a port with a stormy past – in the 16th and 17th centuries, it was a magnet for pillaging pirates! Spanish settlers seized the riches and gold of Colombia's native people, and pirates sieged treasure-laden boats when they docked in the city's port.

REYKJAVÍK

ICELAND Europe

With much of the country covered in snow and volcanoes, Iceland is known as the land of 'ice and fire'. Reykjavík sits on the western shores of Iceland and is surrounded by volatile volcanoes and Arctic animals.

DRAW A PUFFIN!
Puffins are a popular sight in Iceland. Can you draw one? See if you can copy the puffin onto the grid below, drawing it in square by square!

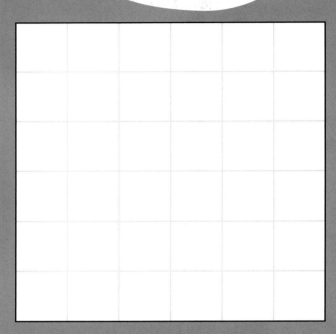

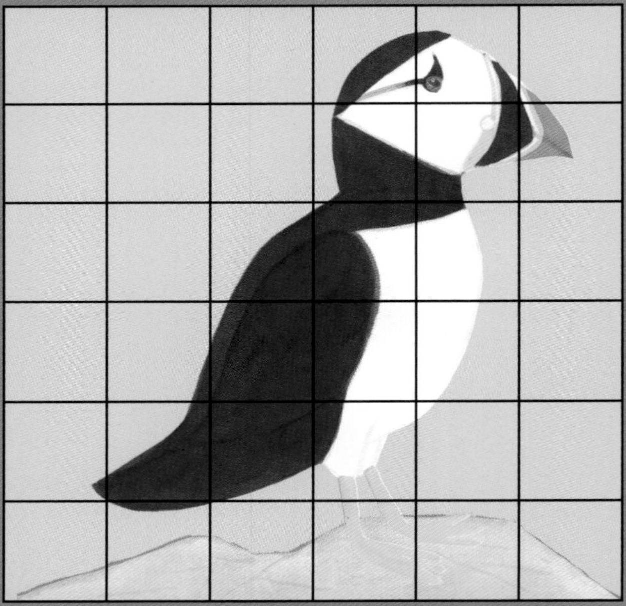

STOCKHOLM

SWEDEN Europe

You have to be crazy about the outdoors to live in Stockholm, a watery city made up of 14 different islands and 57 bridges. In summer it hardly gets dark at all.

COLOUR IN!
Stockholm landmarks include the City Hall (Stadshuset) and the colourful houses of the city's Old Town, known as Gamla Stan. Grab your pencils and add some bright colours!

COPENHAGEN

DENMARK Europe

STICK THE STICKERS!
At Tivoli Gardens a wooden rollercoaster wows visitors. Find the stickers and add some thrillseeking passengers in open cars enjoying the ride!

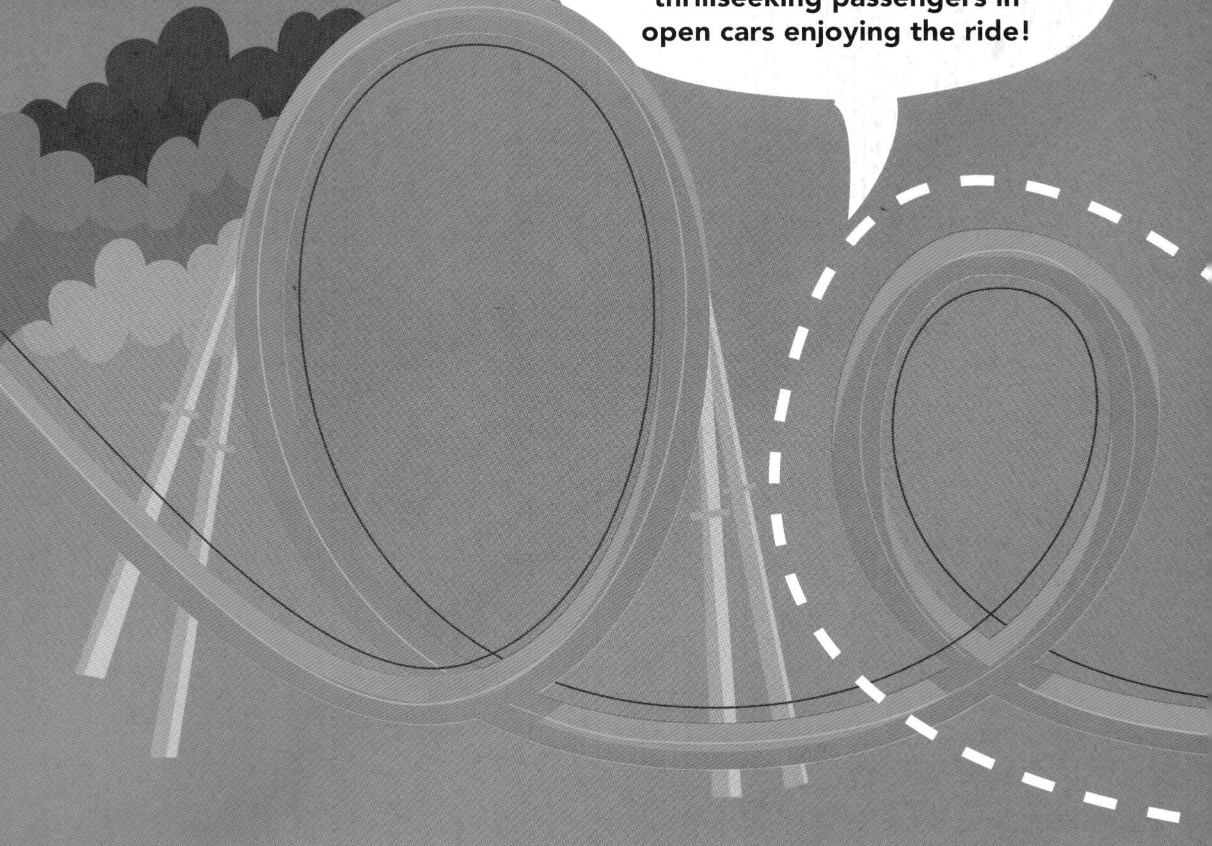

According to a recent report, Copenhagen is one of the happiest places on the planet! Surrounded by sandy beaches and epic play parks, it's easy to see why people love to live here.

AMSTERDAM

NETHERLANDS Europe

Mellow Amsterdam on the Amstel river delta is one of Europe's most beautiful cities. Its streets are peppered with bridges, canals and quaint cafés.

SPOT THE DIFFERENCE!
Thirty-eight per cent of all trips in Amsterdam are made by bike! Can you spot six differences between these biking families?

EDINBURGH

SCOTLAND Europe

Scotland's capital has a medieval old town and it sits in the shadow of an extinct volcano called Arthur's Seat. Edinburgh loves a party, hosting the biggest arts festival in the world. It rains a lot here, but don't be surprised to see men running around in tartan skirts, known as kilts, which are worn for special occasions – though some people wear them all the time.

ADD STICKERS TO COMPLETE THE OUTFIT!
Find the stickers for this man's kilt, hat, socks and shoes – and stick them in here!

LONDON

ENGLAND Europe

London is an urban livewire of grand monuments, glitzy West End theatres and a headline-grabbing royal family. The River Thames winds through the busy city and pigeons bob along the busy streets.

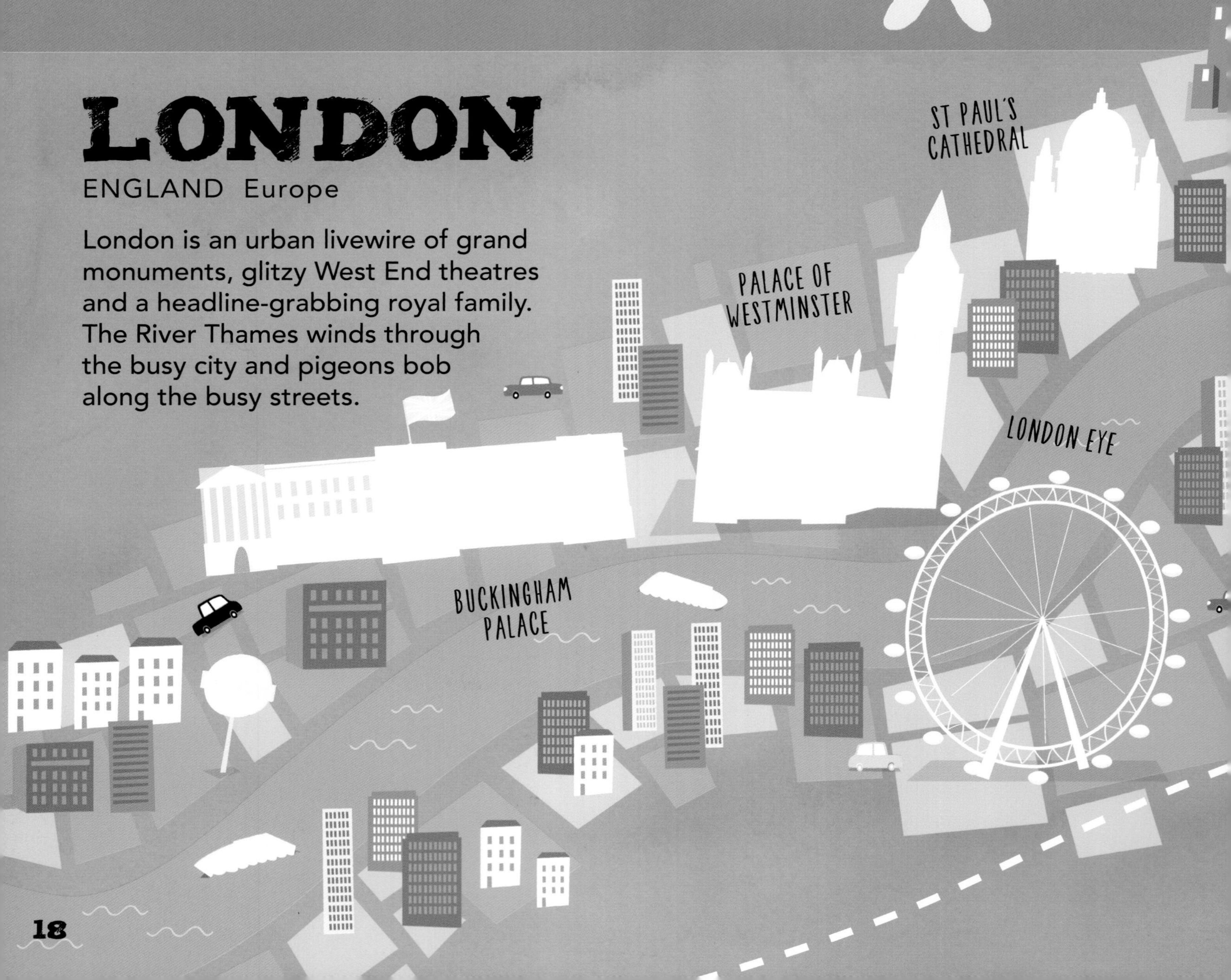

DUBLIN

IRELAND Europe

Dubliners are a famously friendly bunch who are always up for the *craic*, the Irish word for 'fun'. The city is an energetic place packed full of great museums, galleries and art festivals.

MATCH THE SILHOUETTES!
Forget soccer, Dublin kids prefer playing Gaelic football. Which silhouettes match these Gaelic football players?

USE STICKERS TO FILL IN THE SIGHTS!
Grab your stickers and fill in the holes to complete the famous sights along the River Thames.

BRUSSELS

BELGIUM Europe

Brussels has two official languages: French and Dutch (there's no such language as 'Belgian'). The city is a smart, cosmopolitan centre renowned for its beer, chocolate, sweet waffles and comic book characters.

FIND THE ODD ONE OUT!

More chocolate is sold at Brussels' International Airport than anywhere in the world! One box of yummy chocolates is different to all the others – can you spot which one?

ADD FIREWORKS!

On 14th July, Parisians celebrate Bastille Day, the national day of France. Fireworks light up the sky around the Eiffel Tower. Grab your pens and draw in some colourful fireworks!

PARIS

FRANCE Europe

No city is as romantic as Paris, the 'City of the Light'. With its famous museums and landmarks, legendary café life and catwalk fashion, Paris is every bit as elegant as people imagine it to be.

VENICE

ITALY Europe

Venice is Europe's most famous labyrinth. Exploring this small Italian city, built from razor-thin alleyways and romantic canals dotted with gondolas, is just like playing an adventure board game!

USE STICKERS TO FILL IN THE SIGHTS!

Grab your stickers and fill in the holes to complete the beautiful sights of Venice!

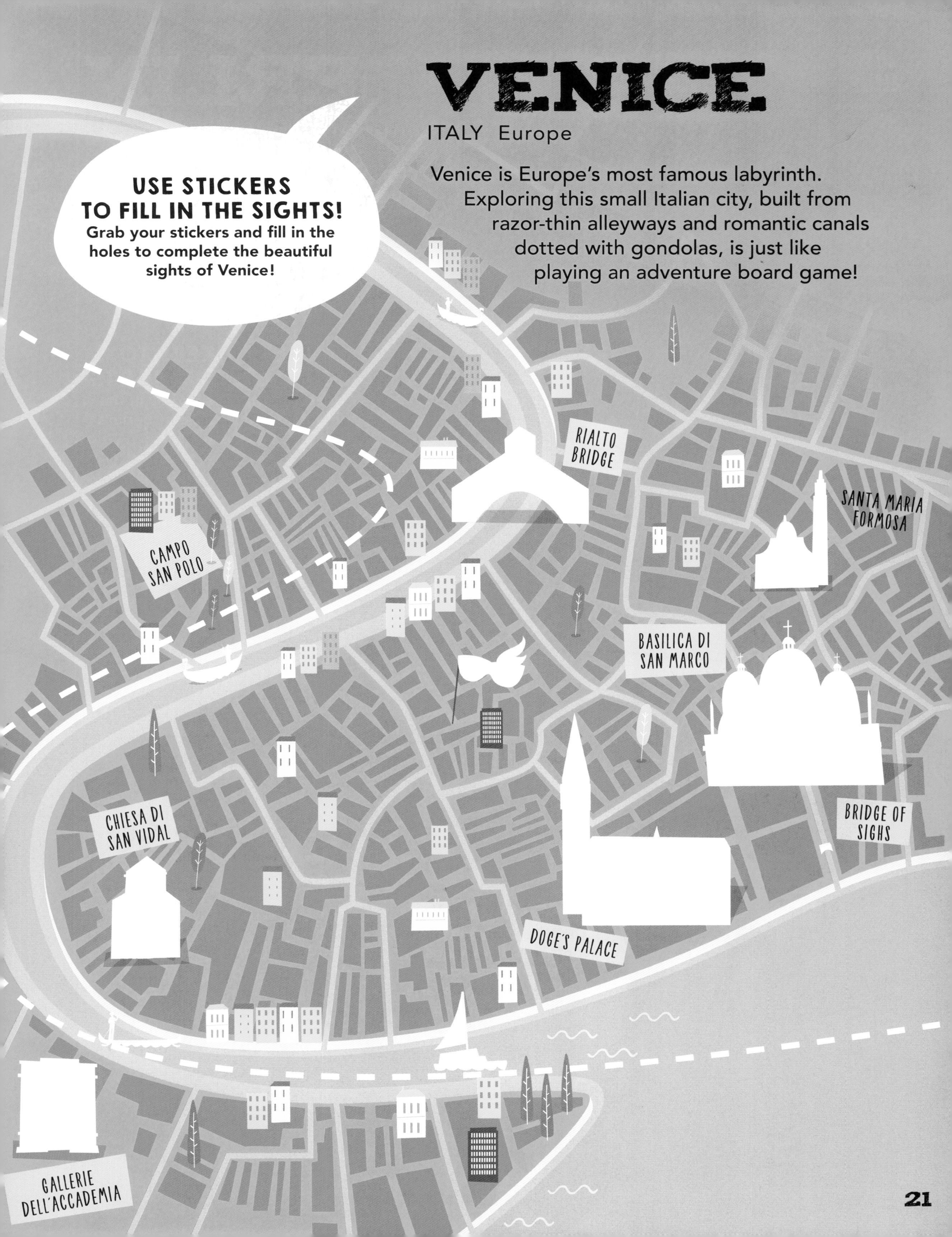

BERLIN

GERMANY Europe

From 1961 to 1990, Berlin was divided by a wall separating communist East Germany from democratic West Germany. Today, the reunited city has an exciting combination of cutting-edge culture and architecture.

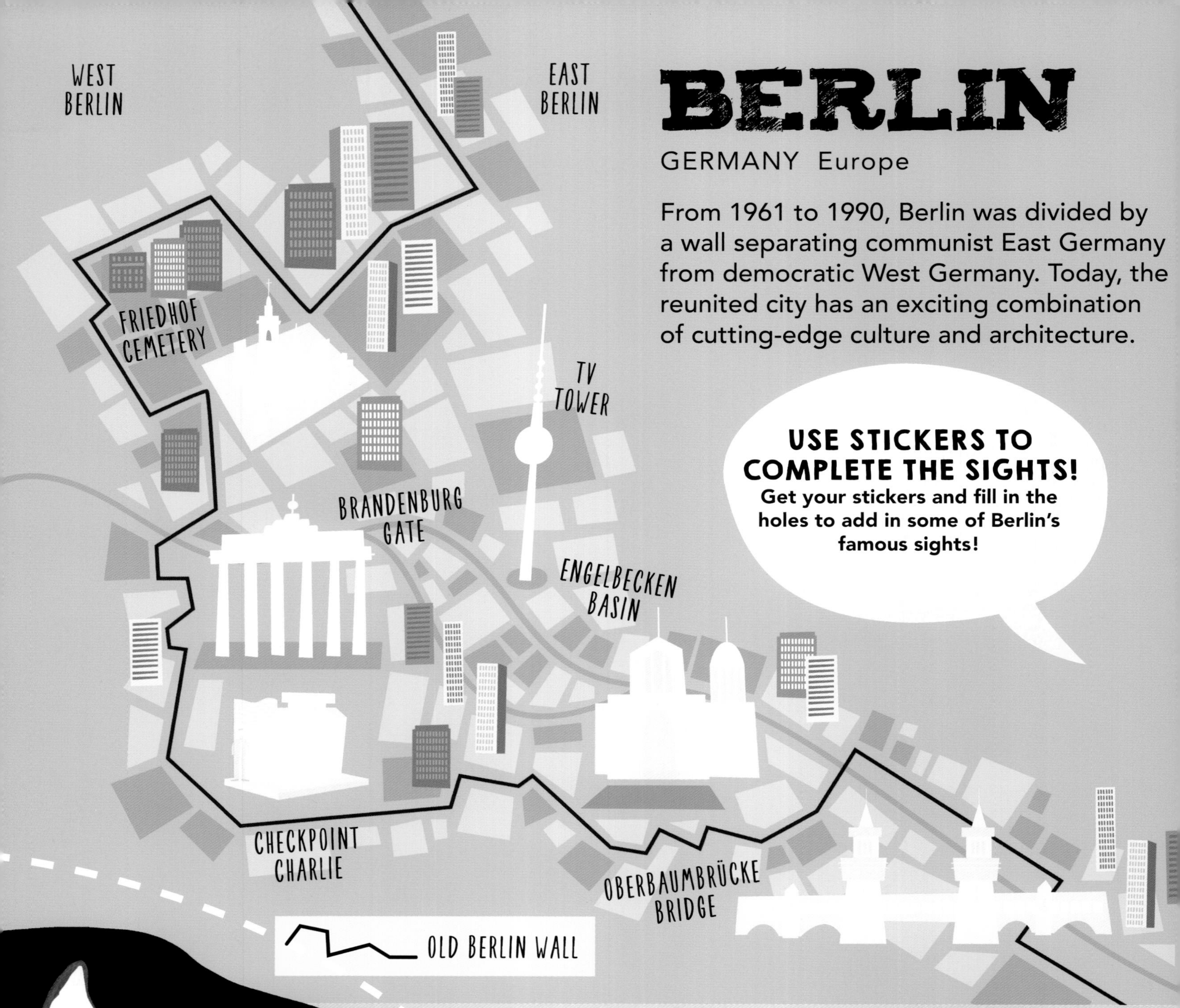

USE STICKERS TO COMPLETE THE SIGHTS!
Get your stickers and fill in the holes to add in some of Berlin's famous sights!

KRAKÓW

POLAND Europe

Kraków is one of the few cities in Poland not to have been destroyed during World War Two. The old town radiates out from Rynek Glowny, Europe's largest medieval market square.

COLOUR IN!
The Wieliczka Salt Mine contains salt carvings of fairy-tale characters. Bring the Seven Dwarfs to life by colouring in these three characters!

VIENNA

AUSTRIA Europe

Vienna is laced with grandiose squares, dazzling palaces and dancing fountains. It's not hard to imagine Mozart, Strauss and other classical composers who once lived here strolling through the streets.

SPOT THE DIFFERENCE!

Spot six differences between these horses and their riders performing a display at Vienna's famous Spanish Riding School.

ATHENS

GREECE Europe

Greece's cosmopolitan city is one of the most historic in the world. Democracy was born in Athens, and the streets now buzz with markets and outdoor cafés.

COUNT THE BOOKS!

A man called Draco recorded the city's first laws in the 7th century BC. How many books can you count behind him?

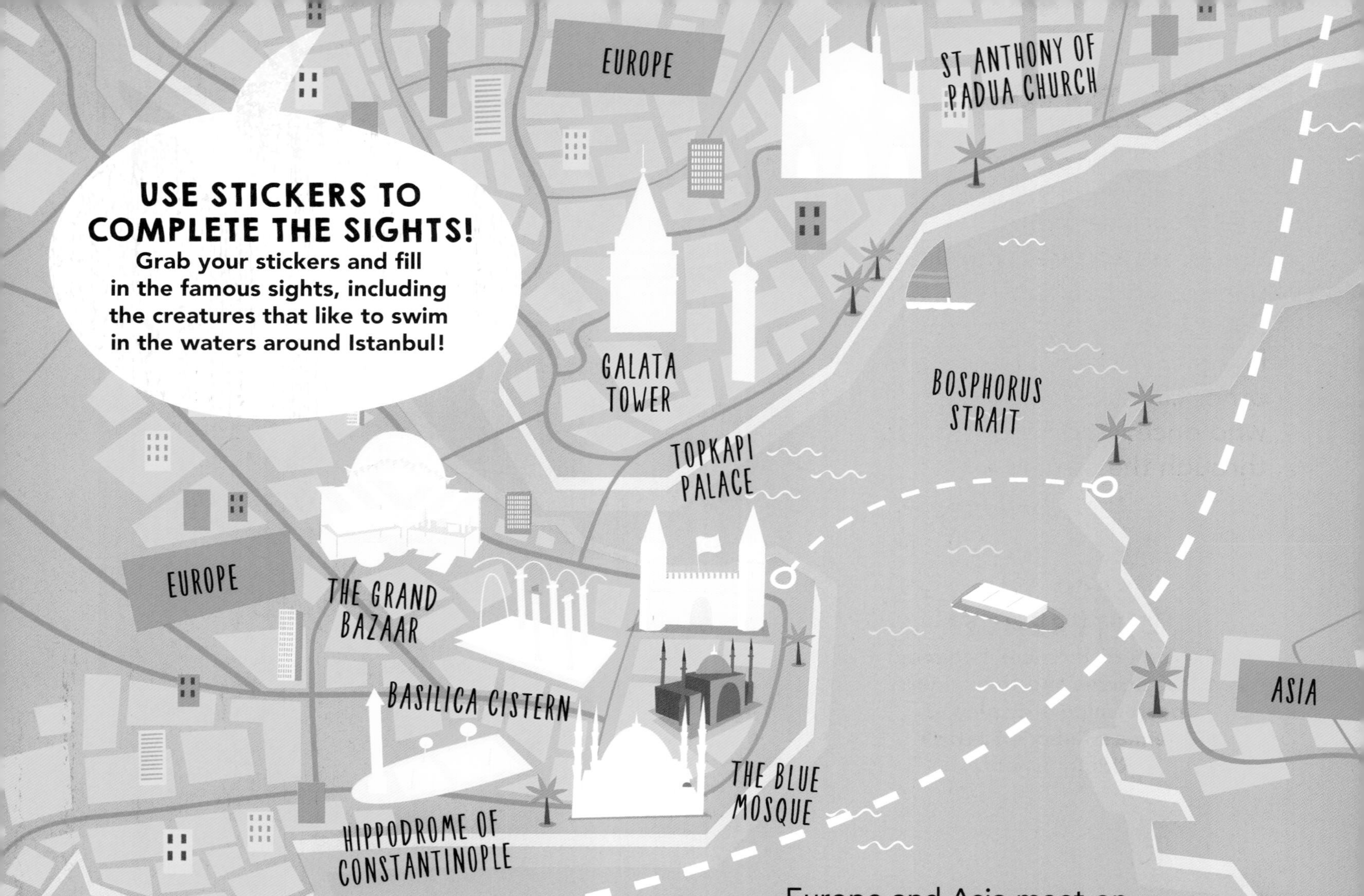

USE STICKERS TO COMPLETE THE SIGHTS!
Grab your stickers and fill in the famous sights, including the creatures that like to swim in the waters around Istanbul!

ISTANBUL

TURKEY Europe

Europe and Asia meet on Istanbul's ancient streets. The skyline twinkles with minarets and mosques, church spires and grand palaces. Three huge bridges cross the Bosphorus Strait to link the two continents.

MADRID

SPAIN Europe

Madrid is like a big child that buzzes with energy and never wants to go to bed. It is also a city of culture and its famous Prado museum is home to some of the finest works of art on the planet.

COUNT THE FISH!
The fish market in Madrid is the biggest in Europe. How many fish can you count?

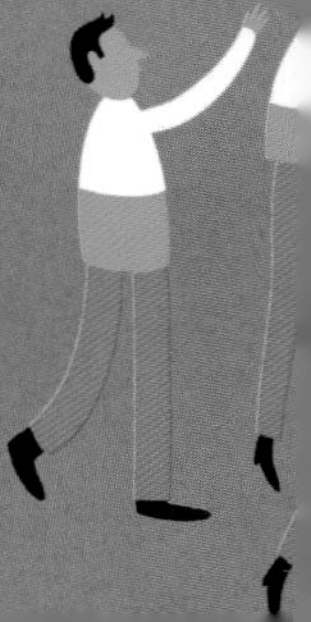

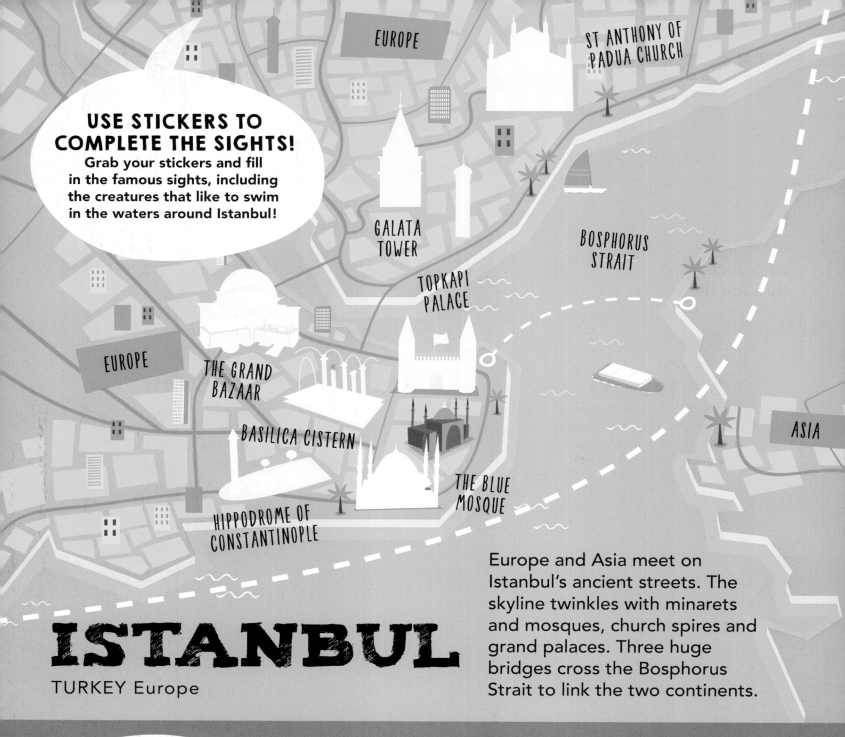

MOSCOW

RUSSIA Europe

Snow covers the pavements of this cold, ancient city during the icy Russian winters. The huge medieval fortress of the Kremlin, home to the Russian government, is located in the city's Red Square, close to St Basil's Cathedral.

COLOUR IN!

The nine colourful domes of St Basil's Cathedral are an unforgettable sight. Colour in the cathedral with eye-catching colours of your choice!

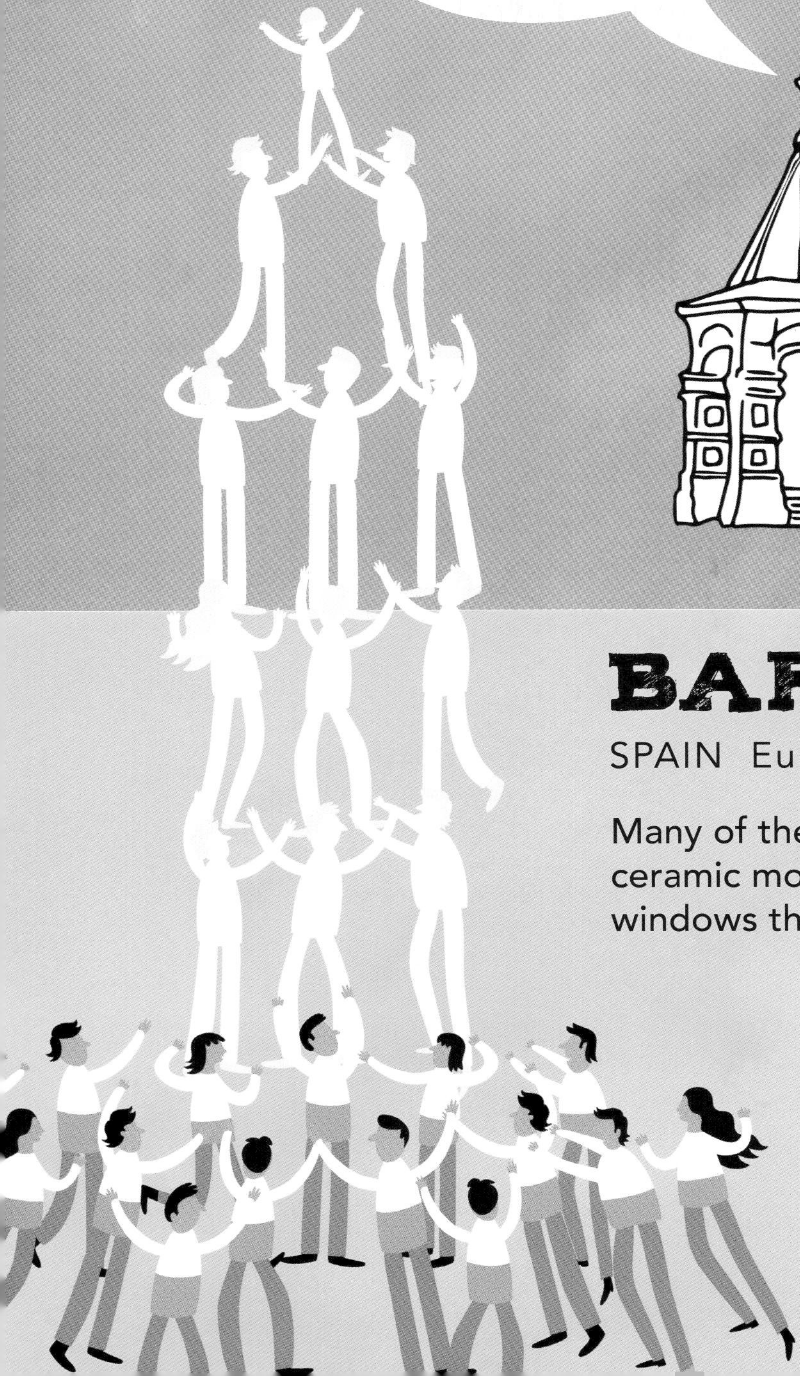

BARCELONA

SPAIN Europe

Many of the buildings in Barcelona are covered in bright ceramic mosaics or have wonderful curved walls and windows that were created by the architect Antoni Gaudí.

ADD PEOPLE STICKERS!

A festival in the city celebrates the sport of building towers out of people! Grab your stickers and add the missing people in the tower!

MARRAKESH

MOROCCO Africa

Hot, hectic and heaving with history, Marrakesh is a head-spinner of a city. The mighty Atlas Mountains look down upon a metropolis that's brimming with North African magic and mayhem.

ADD STICKERS!
The busy marketplace of Djemaa El-Fna is packed with performers, snake charmers and street-sellers. Grab your stickers and complete the bustling scene!

TIMBUKTU

MALI Africa

This ancient city basks on the red-hot southern rim of the Sahara Desert. In Timbuktu, the streets are made of sand, and motor vehicles are massively outnumbered by donkeys and camels.

LINK THE TRAILS!
At night, aardvarks forage around the city looking for ants and termites. Can you match the aardvark trail with the correct termite nest?

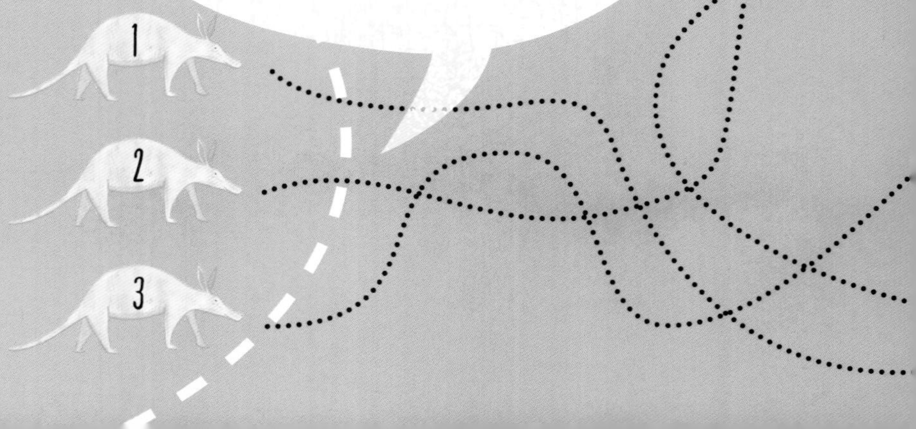

ADDIS ABABA

ETHIOPIA Africa

Ethiopia's capital is a city of contrasts, where shepherds lead animals past high-tech tower blocks. Sections of this rapidly growing metropolis are booming. Poverty, however, remains a terrible reality – an estimated 60,000 kids live on the city's streets.

WRITE A RAP!

Modern music like hip-hop is becoming increasingly popular in Addis Ababa. Can you come up with your own rap? It might be inspired by events in your life, friends or heroes. Write down the lyrics here!

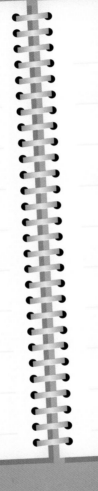

CAIRO

EGYPT Africa

Egypt's capital sprawls across a site that's been populated for thousands of years. Across the river Nile from modern Cairo is one of the most famous historical sites in the world – the Giza Pyramid Complex. This site boasts three giant pyramids, including the Great Pyramid, once the tallest building on the planet.

BUILD A PYRAMID!

Find the stickers and fill in the holes to complete the pyramid below! Can you also find the other stickers to complete the desert scene?

NAIROBI

KENYA Africa

Nairobi is developing at lightning speed, but nature never strays too far away. Monkeys swing through parks close to modern shopping malls, and wildebeest graze amongst grasses on the outskirts of the city.

DESIGN YOUR OWN MATATU!

Nairobi teems with colourful *matatu* (minibuses). Find the stickers and stick on your own eye-popping design, and use pens to colour in the rest!

ADD STICKERS TO FILL IN THE SIGHTS!

It's all hustle and bustle in Dakar, while humpback whales splash in the surrounding sea. Find the stickers and fill in the holes to complete the city view!

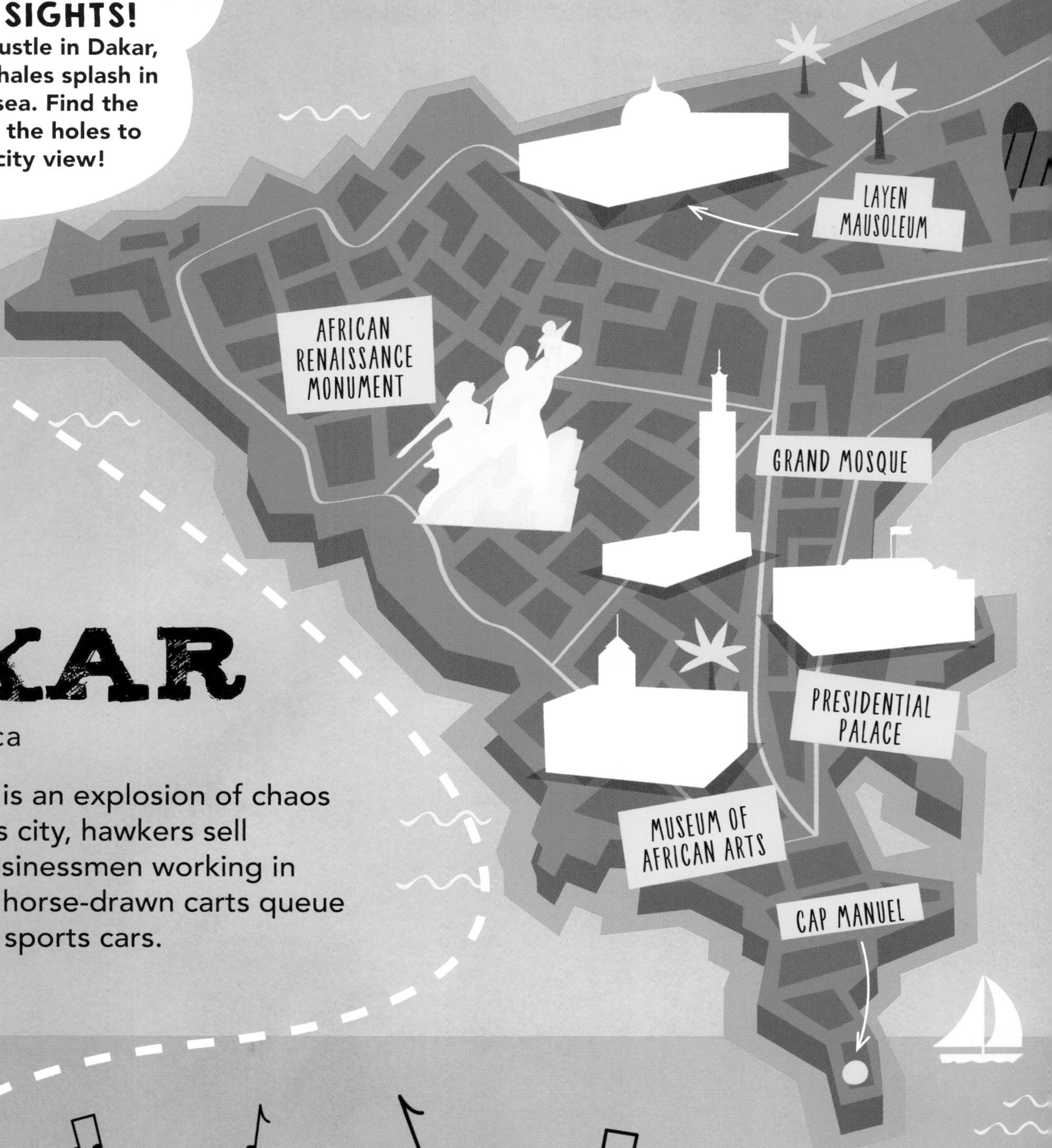

DAKAR

SENEGAL Africa

Senegal's capital is an explosion of chaos and colour. In this city, hawkers sell street food to businessmen working in skyscrapers, and horse-drawn carts queue up next to flashy sports cars.

ZANZIBAR TOWN

TANZANIA Africa

Modern Zanzibar Town is packed with office blocks and businesses. The older heart of the tropical city has crumbling coral-stone palaces, forts, mosques and a seafront market where kids slurp on fruity sugarcane smoothies.

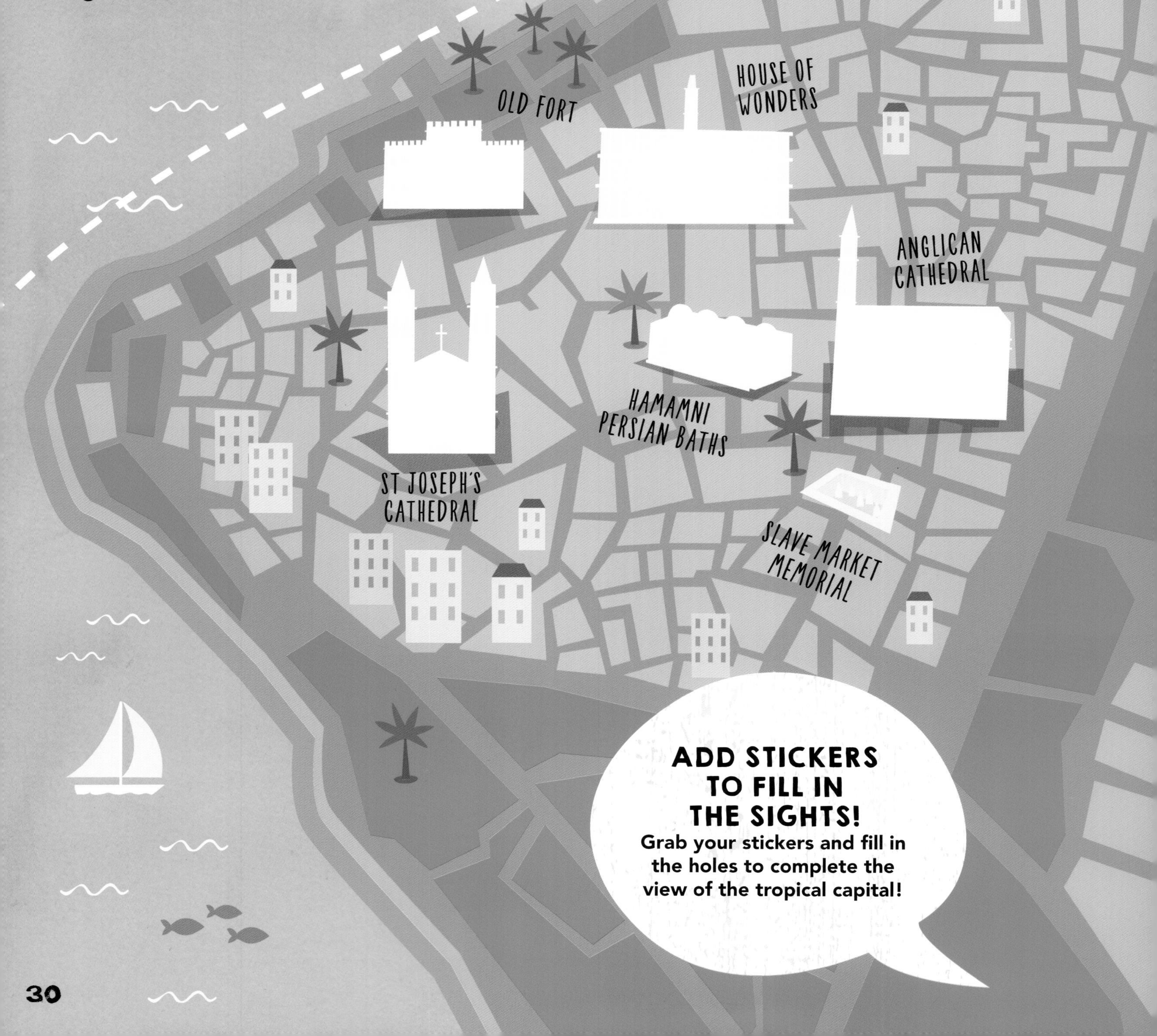

ADD STICKERS TO FILL IN THE SIGHTS!

Grab your stickers and fill in the holes to complete the view of the tropical capital!

CAPE TOWN

SOUTH AFRICA Africa

Cape Town stretches out under a flat-topped mountain called Table Mountain. The city lies next to a stunning sweep of green vineyards and sandy bays. In the city's District Six, street art celebrates the rainbow nation's heroes.

DRAW A PORTRAIT!

Nelson Mandela (seen here) did the most to topple Apartheid, a system that discriminates against black people. Copy the portrait of Nelson Mandela below, using the grid as a guide, box by box.

JERUSALEM

ISRAEL/PALESTINIAN TERRITORIES Asia

One of the planet's oldest settlements, Jerusalem is very important to three of the world's biggest religions (Judaism, Christianity and Islam). Because both Israel and the Palestinian Territories claim it as their capital, Jerusalem is often the site of conflict – but life goes on in this vibrant city.

- THE NUMBER 103
- A MAN WAVING
- A WATER BOTTLE
- A BOWL OF BLACK OLIVES
- A BLACK BIRD
- A MAN TALKING ON A MOBILE PHONE

CAN YOU SPOT?
There are colourful murals all over the city and many are painted as optical illusions. Can you spot these six items in the picture? Add a smiley sticker for each one!

MECCA

SAUDI ARABIA Asia

Mecca is the centre of the Islamic universe. During Dhu-al-Hijjah (the holy month) the city's population swells by millions as Muslims make a *Hajj* (pilgrimage) to the city's ultra-sacred Kaaba (a holy shrine).

DECORATE THE CAMEL!
During the *Hajj*, camels are decorated with wreaths of flowers and bright ribbons. Colour in this camel, adding some dazzling decorations as you go.

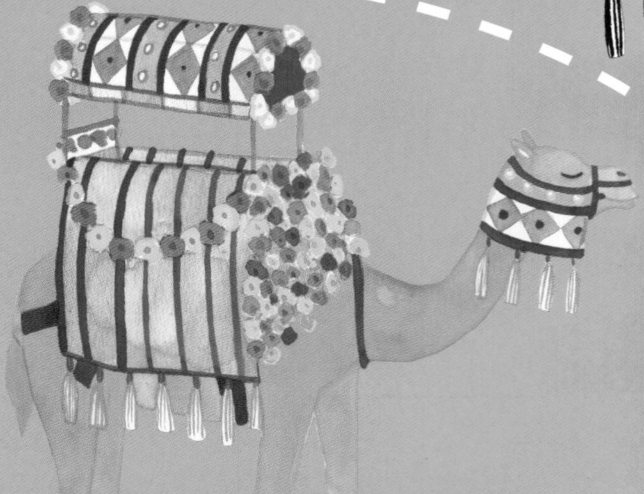

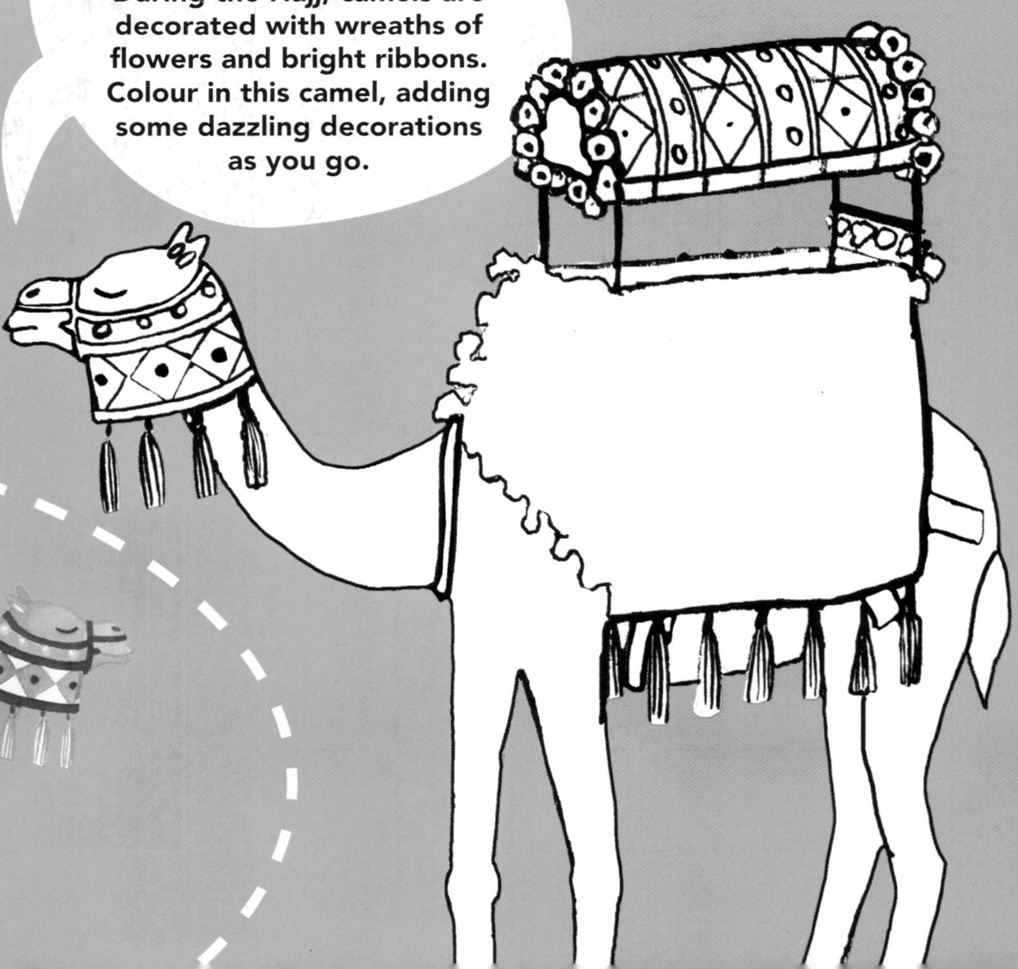

DUBAI

UNITED ARAB EMIRATES Asia

Dubai is now an ultra-modern metropolis standing in the sand of the United Arab Emirates, with loads of fancy shops and some of the most amazing and ambitious buildings on the planet.

THE TALLEST BUILDINGS!
The Burj Khalifa in Dubai is the tallest building on the planet. Find the building stickers and put the world's tallest structures in height order.

SHANGHAI TOWER, SHANGHAI, CHINA

ONE WORLD TRADE CENTER, NEW YORK, USA

SHANGHAI WORLD FINANCE CENTER, SHANGHAI, CHINA

BURJ KHALIFA, DUBAI

MAKKAH ROYAL CLOCK TOWER, MECCA, SAUDI ARABIA

TAIPEI 101, TAIPEI, CHINA

SAMARKAND

UZBEKISTAN Asia

This 2,700-year-old metropolis reached its peak in the 14th century under the legendary Mongol warlord Timur (also known as Tamerlane). Today, Uzbekistan's most glorious and magical city boasts incredible squares, buildings and bazaars.

ADD THE STAR STICKERS!
The lack of light pollution makes Samarkand a great place to gaze at stars. Find the star stickers and fill the sky with twinkling light!

USE STICKERS TO FILL IN THE SIGHTS!
Varanasi is all about the sacred River Ganges. Grab your stickers and fill in the holes to complete this vibrant riverbank scene!

MUMBAI

INDIA Asia

The mega-city of Mumbai, formerly known as Bombay, is home to 21 million people. A densely populated city, Mumbai is also India's richest metropolis, teeming with workers and businesses.

SPOT THE DIFFERENCE!
Mumbai is the centre of India's famous Bollywood film industry. Can you spot five differences between these Bollywood dancers?

VARANASI

INDIA Asia

Varanasi is India's oldest city and the holiest place in the Hindu faith, clustered around the River Ganges. To die or be cremated here is seen as a great blessing. Thousands come to the river to bathe, pray and perform rituals on ghats (sets of steps leading down into the water).

BĚIJĪNG

CHINA Asia

Běijīng bounces to the beat of 21 million people working and playing under a sometimes smoggy sky. The former imperial place known as the Forbidden City is a reminder of this mega-city's extraordinary history.

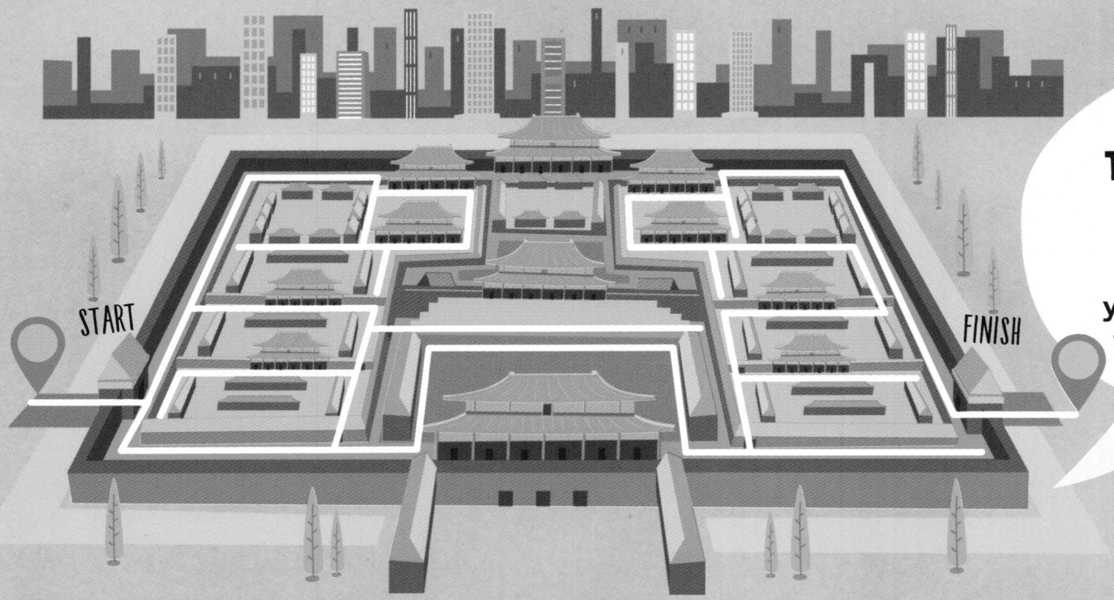

FIND YOUR WAY THROUGH THE MAZE!

There are many buildings scattered throughout the Forbidden City. Can you find your way along the white paths through the maze of buildings from start to finish?

HONG KONG

CHINA Asia

Hong Kong is one of the richest cities in the world – a forest of skyscrapers rising up from a few small islands off the south coast of China. The streets are a heady mix of

CHÉNGDŪ

CHINA Asia

The capital of China's Sichuān region seems happy to keep a low profile. Chéngdū is filled with laid-back teahouses and restaurants serving spicy noodles.

SPOT THE DIFFERENCE!

The mountains around Sichuān are home to the giant panda. Can you spot five differences between these two bamboo-munching pandas?

ULAANBAATAR

MONGOLIA Asia

This vibrant city is a throbbing pulse in a surrounding wilderness. It's a cold, colourful place where young people with Mohican haircuts mingle with Buddhist monks and suited professionals share the streets with visiting nomads.

ADD STICKERS!

Ulaanbaatar may be the world's coldest capital, but many people there still live in traditional felt tents called *gers*. Find the *ger* stickers and stick them in to complete the city scene!

SWITCH ON THE LIGHTS!

After dark, the streets in Hong Kong are ablaze with lights. Grab some highlighter pens and colour in the skyscraper windows to set the city alight!

BANGKOK

THAILAND Asia

Bangkok is one of the hottest, busiest, hungriest and most thrilling places on Earth. From revving bike taxis, called *tuktuks*, to crowded canals – this is a city on the go, all day, every day.

CAN YOU SPOT?
Canals in the city are used for floating markets. Can you spot the things below in this picture? Add a smiley sticker next to each one you find!

- A MAN WITH A RED SCARF
- A PERSON IN A CHECKED SHIRT
- A PERSON TOUCHING THEIR HAT
- A SET OF SAUCEPANS
- TOURISTS TAKING PICTURES
- A GREEN CONTAINER ON A STICK

DRAW IN PEOPLE!
Singapore has the world's first nocturnal zoo. Grab some pens and draw in some passengers riding a tram past the animals!

SINGAPORE

SINGAPORE Asia

Singapore isn't just a city – it's a whole country! Alongside Monaco and the Vatican City, this ultra-modern metropolis is one of the world's few city-states and is one of Asia's richest cities.

HANOI

VIETNAM Asia

Vietnam's capital is pulsing and prosperous and full of surprises! Street vendors carry baskets balanced on poles and serene locals practise a martial art called t'ai chi on the shores of Lake Hoan Kiem.

INVENT YOUR OWN BUNS!

Hanoians eat *bánh bao*: sweet, steamed buns filled with chicken, quail eggs and other fillings. What flavour fillings would you put in a bun? Write them down here!

MY BUN'S NAME: ....

FILLINGS:

MANILA

PHILIPPINES Asia

Manila is mammoth – a vast, sprawling metropolis that appears to never end. With its beautiful Spanish buildings, resourceful people and truly astonishing food, the city deserves its reputation as the 'Pearl of the Orient'.

FIND THE WAY OUT!

Underneath the city is a huge network of tunnels. Help the people below get back to the surface!

COUNT THE COMMUTERS!
Tokyo's metro system is super-busy and guards push people onto packed trains. How many passengers can you count on this train?

TOKYO

JAPAN Asia

Tokyo is the most populated, fastest, flashiest city on Earth. Days are filled with the early noise of the Tsukiji Fish Market, the whir of the commuter trains, the cheers of sumo wrestling fans and the beat of karaoke bars.

ADD BLOSSOM STICKERS!
In early spring in Kyoto, cherry blossoms burst out of the trees. Find the blossom stickers and stick them here to fill the tree with flowers!

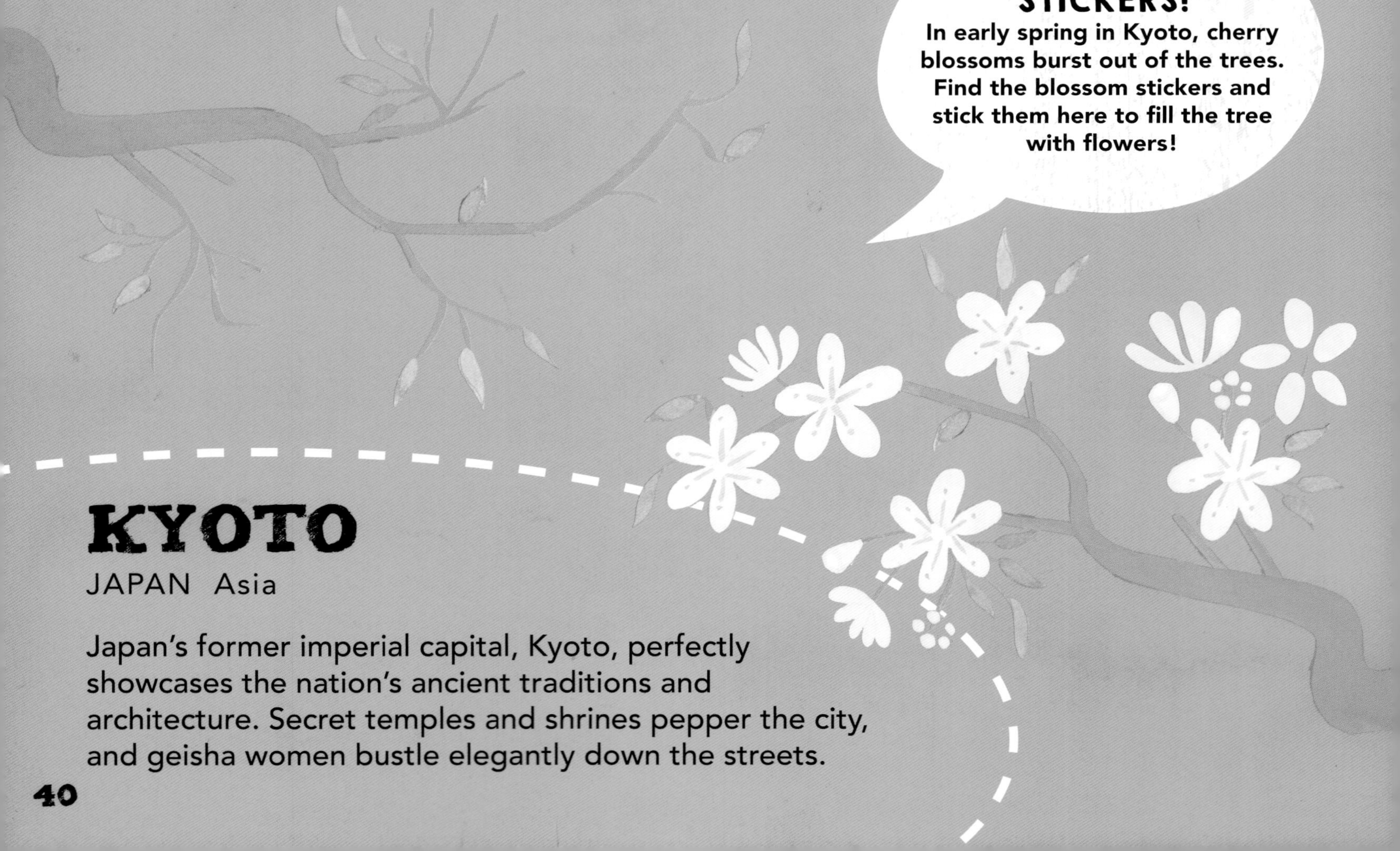

KYOTO

JAPAN Asia

Japan's former imperial capital, Kyoto, perfectly showcases the nation's ancient traditions and architecture. Secret temples and shrines pepper the city, and geisha women bustle elegantly down the streets.

PYONGYANG

NORTH KOREA Asia

Capital of communist-run North Korea, Pyongyang is a fascinating and secretive city of monumental buildings and public festivals. Its modern skyline includes Ryugyong Hotel, a pyramid-shaped tower of over 330 m (1,082 ft).

DO THE DOT-TO-DOT!
Join the dots to reveal Pyongyang's most eye-catching building!

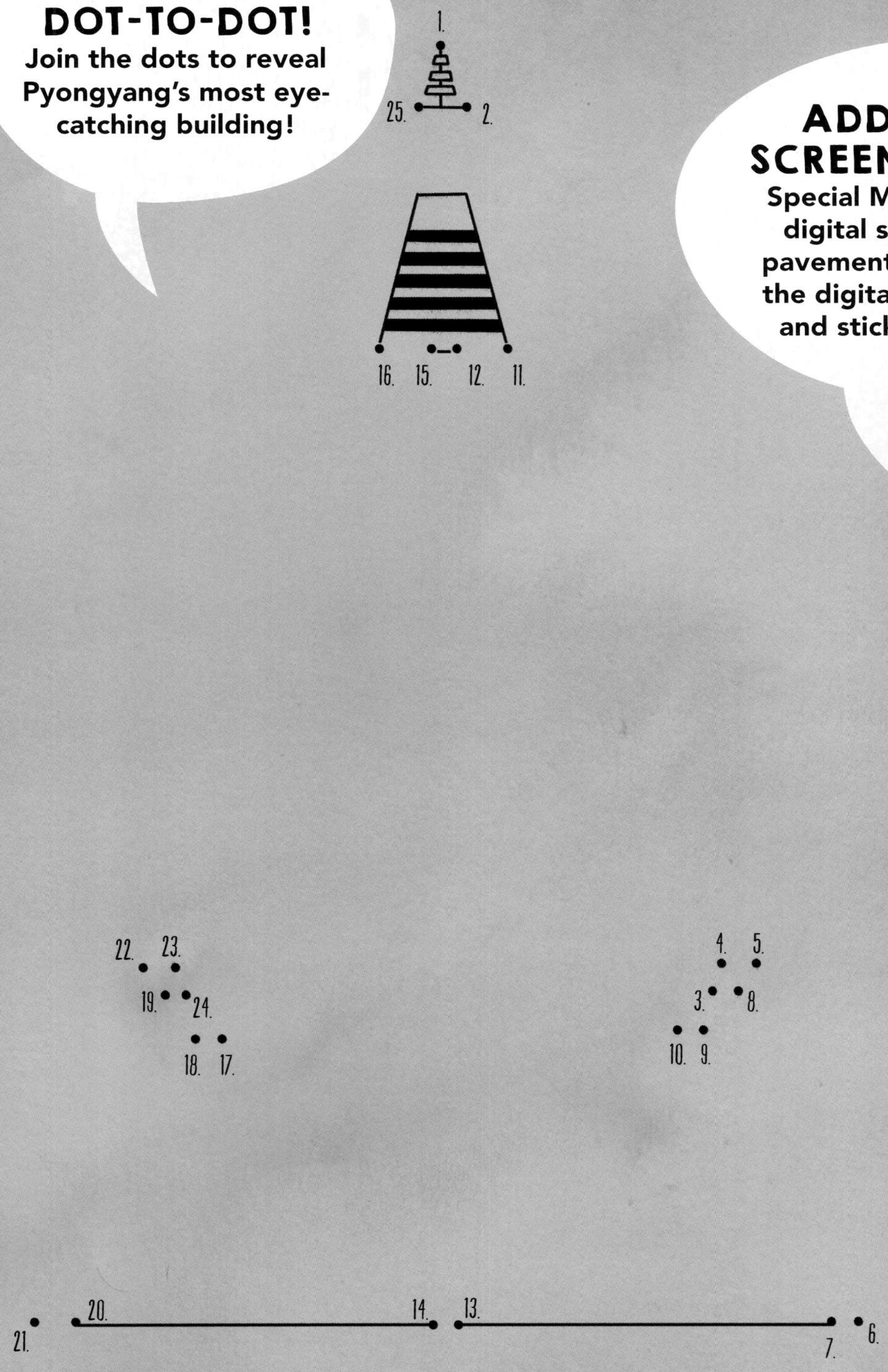

SEOUL

SOUTH KOREA Asia

Seoul's growth and wealth have skyrocketed since the 1950s and life is sweet in this forward-facing city. Classic pagodas and teahouses mingle with shining towers, digital screens and bright neon signs.

ADD DIGITAL SCREEN STICKERS!
Special Media Poles with digital screens line the pavements in Seoul. Grab the digital screen stickers and stick them in here!

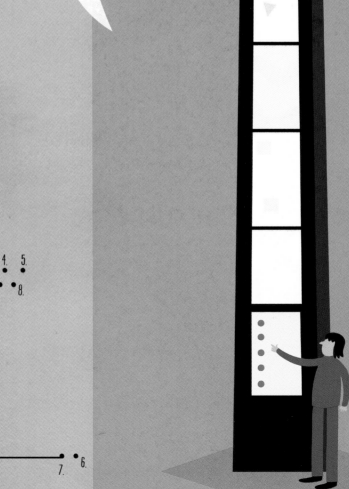

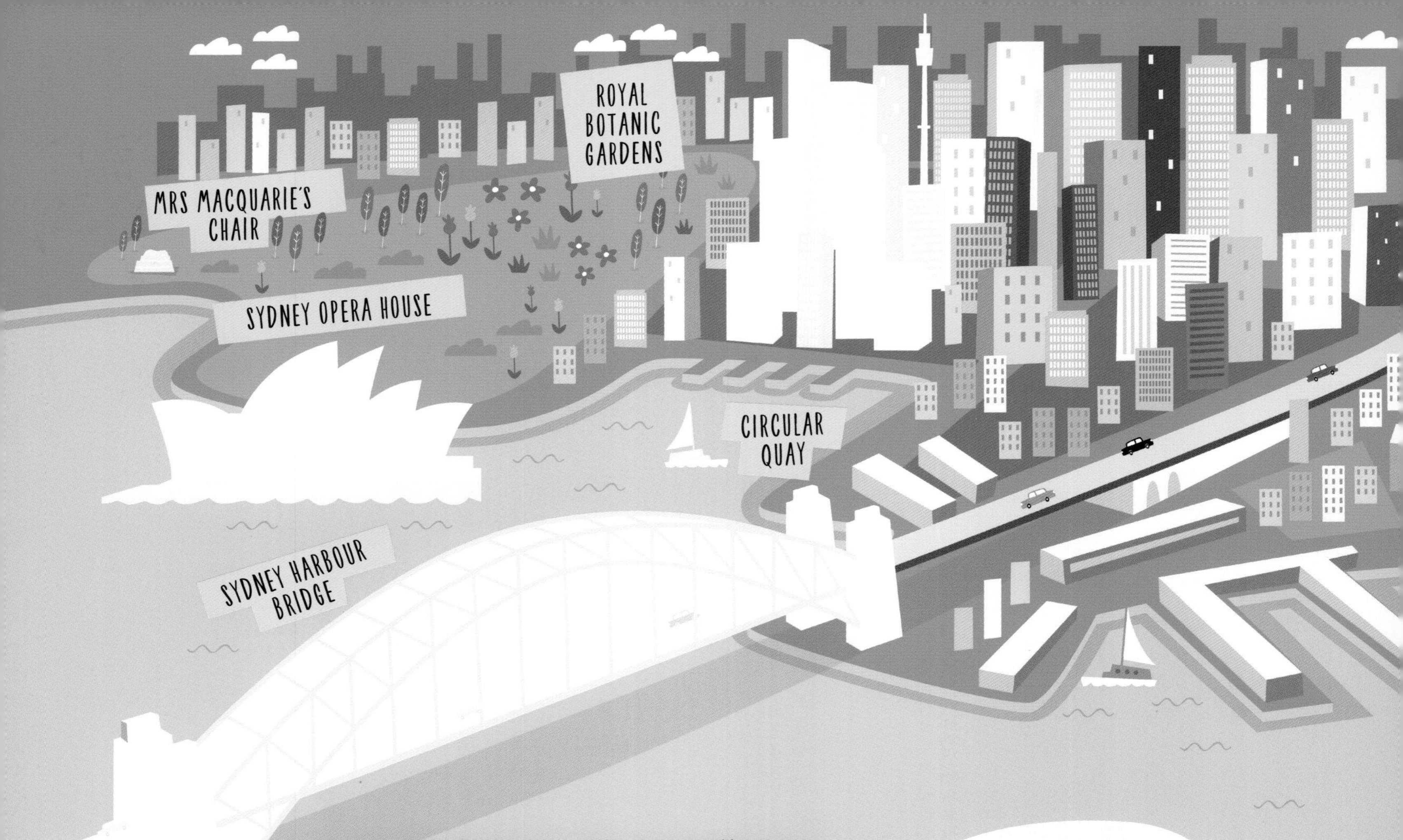

SYDNEY

AUSTRALIA Oceania

The beautiful city of Sydney curves around the largest natural harbour in the world. Iconic landmarks sparkle in the sunshine, beaches bustle with surfers and restaurants serve up fabulous fusion food.

USE STICKERS TO FILL IN THE SIGHTS!
Grab your stickers and fill in the holes to complete the view of Sydney.

DARWIN

AUSTRALIA Oceania

Sultry, remote and multicultural, Darwin is Australia's only tropical city. Nature is here in all its wild variety, from the dramatic beauty of Darwin's national parks to the brooding menace of the saltwater crocodiles that hunt in the harbour.

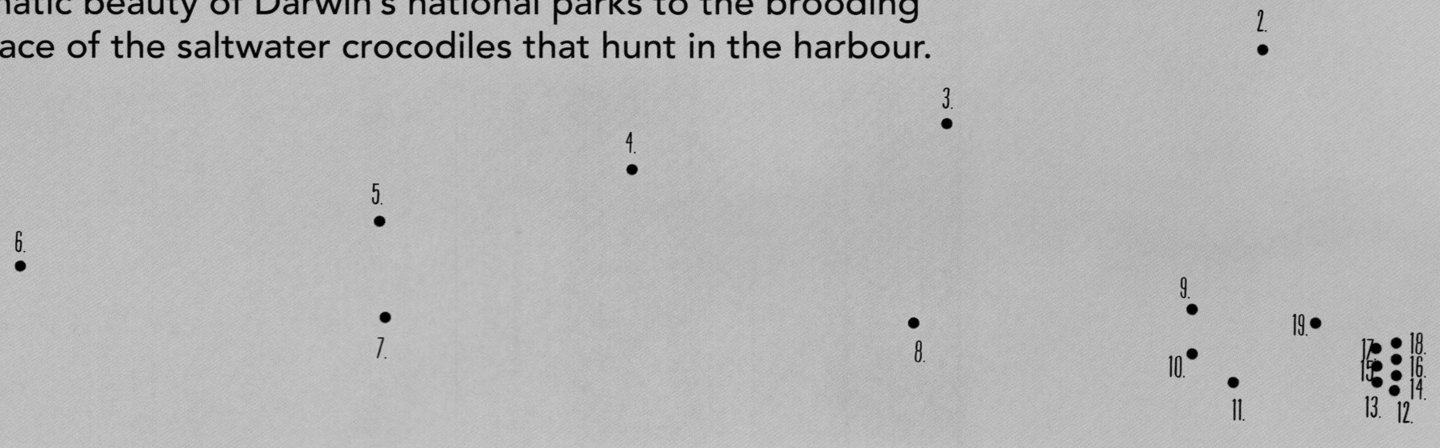

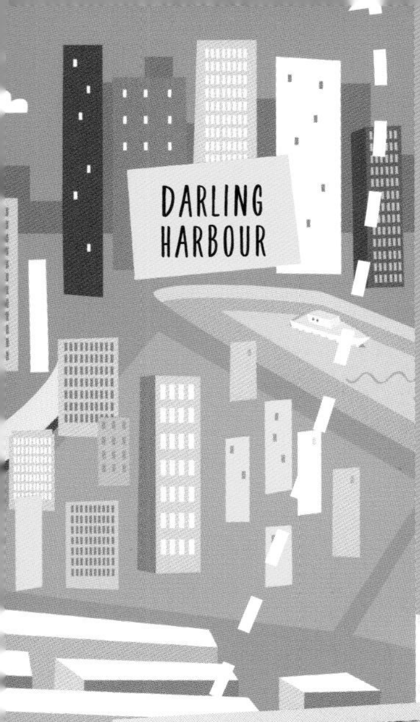

MELBOURNE

AUSTRALIA Oceania

Melbourne is one of a kind – a proud Australian city with a cool, European vibe. It was only founded in 1835, but it has made a name for itself as a prosperous town that loves its art and its sport in equal measure.

PAINT THE WALL!
Melbourne encourages graffiti artists to decorate blank walls in the city with murals. Add your own design here!

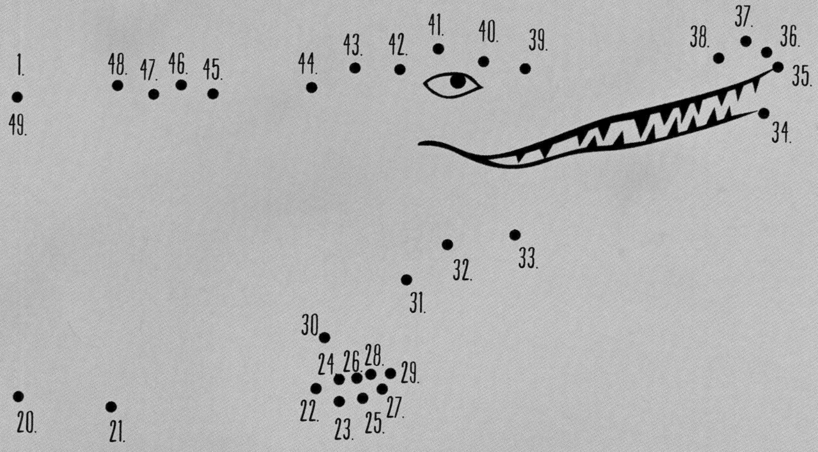

DOT THE CROC!
Crocodiles often lurk on the mudbanks of Darwin Harbour. Join the dots to complete the picture of this ancient predator.

AUCKLAND

NEW ZEALAND Oceania

While Auckland is not New Zealand's capital – that honour goes to Wellington – it is the country's biggest city. With the world's biggest Polynesian population, a growing Asian community and native Maori people, the city also has an international feel.

ADD THE STICKERS!
Grab your stickers and complete the outfits of people doing a traditional Maori dance.

ADD SOME BOATS!
The waterfront of Auckland is packed with boats, from yachts to catamarans. Draw in some boats bobbing on the water!

APIA

SAMOA Oceania

Once a tiny fishing village on the island of Upolu, Apia is now the capital of the Pacific nation of Samoa. It sits in a natural harbour lined with white sandy beaches and volcanic mountains.

DRAW A BLACK MARLIN!
Living slap-bang in the middle of a big ocean, Samoans eat a lot of fish! Copy the picture of this black marlin box by box!

QUEENSTOWN

NEW ZEALAND Oceania

Queenstown's dramatic scenery is world famous, although the city has plenty more to offer. Gap year students brave bungee jumps and families sunbathe along the sandy strip. Maori culture is also woven into modern life in the city.

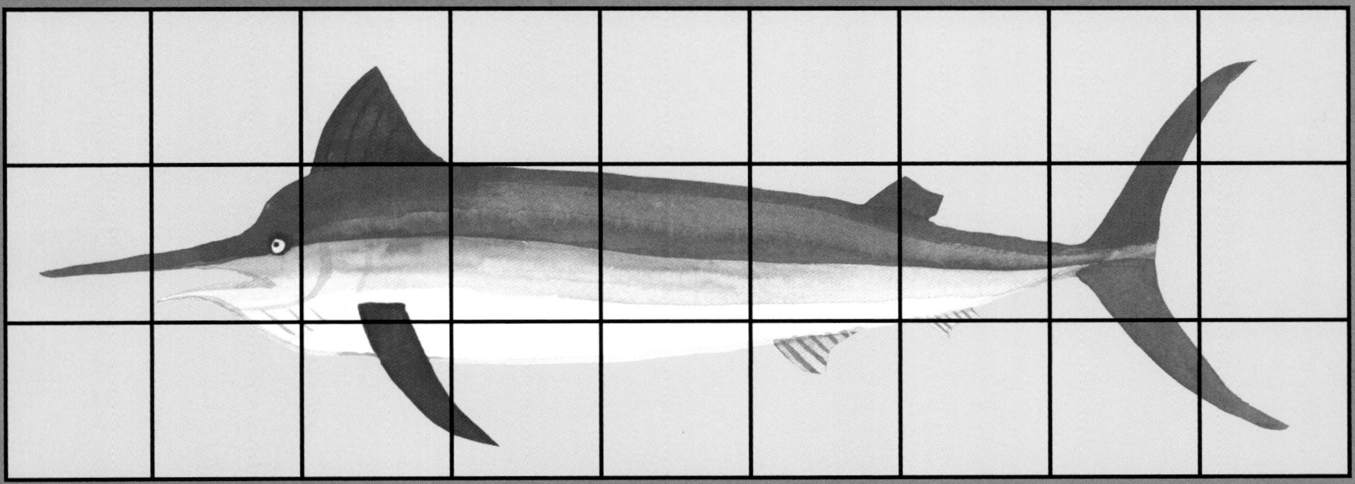

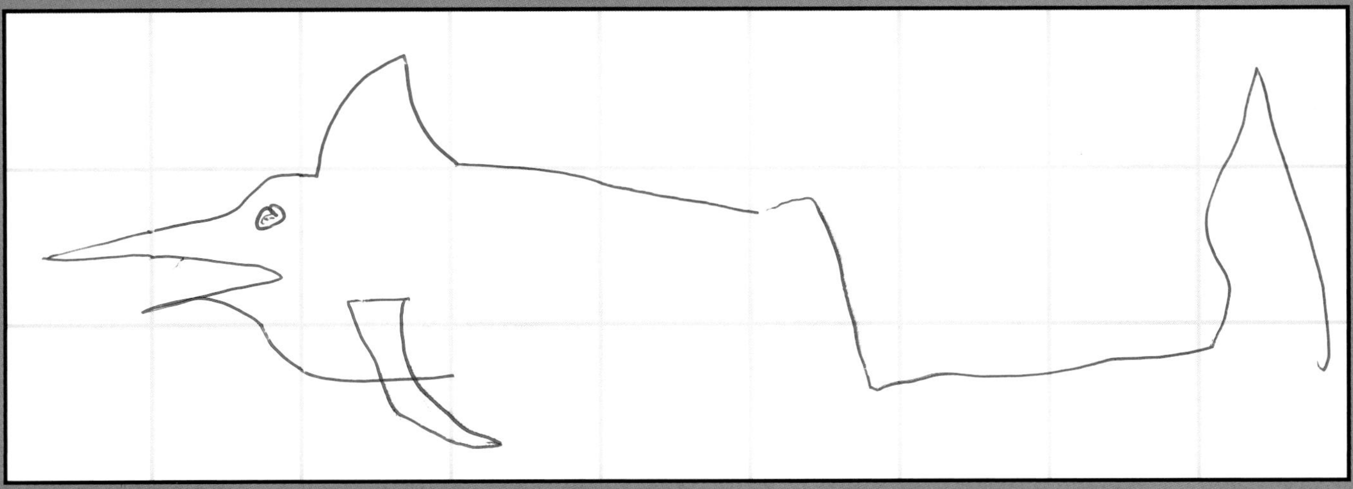

ANSWERS

4 MONTRÉAL

11 OAXACA CITY

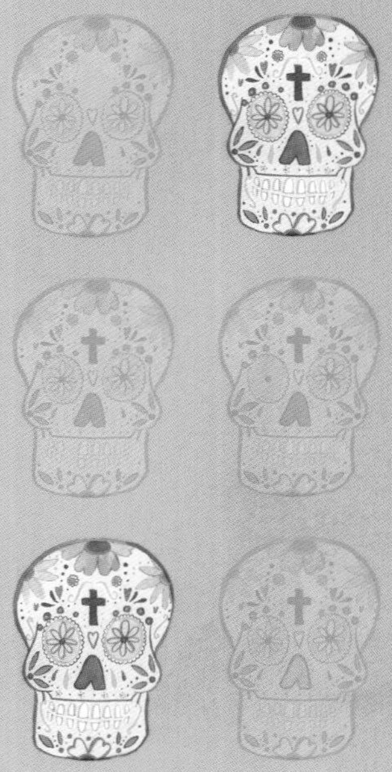

13 MANAUS

There are 240 spider legs.

4 TORONTO

There are 11 islands.

7 WASHINGTON, DC

There are 24 windows.

9 SAN FRANCISCO

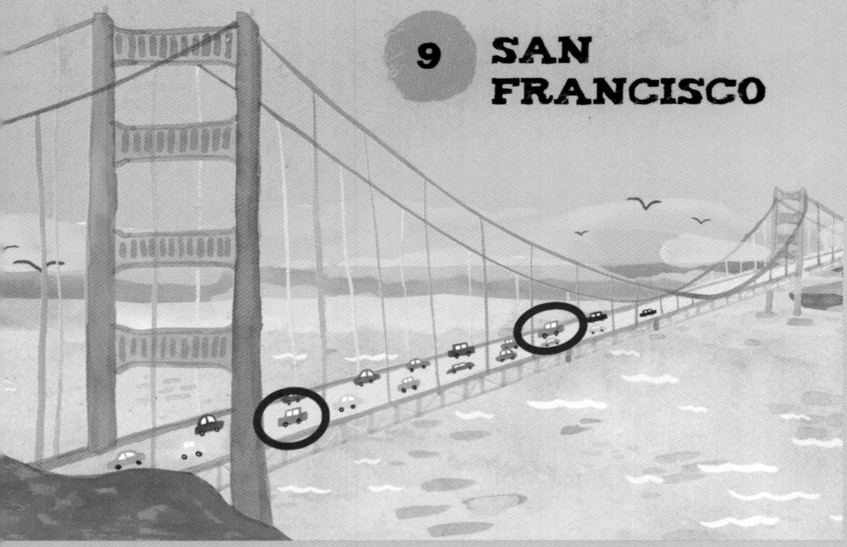

13 CUZCO

14 USHUAIA

10 HAVANA

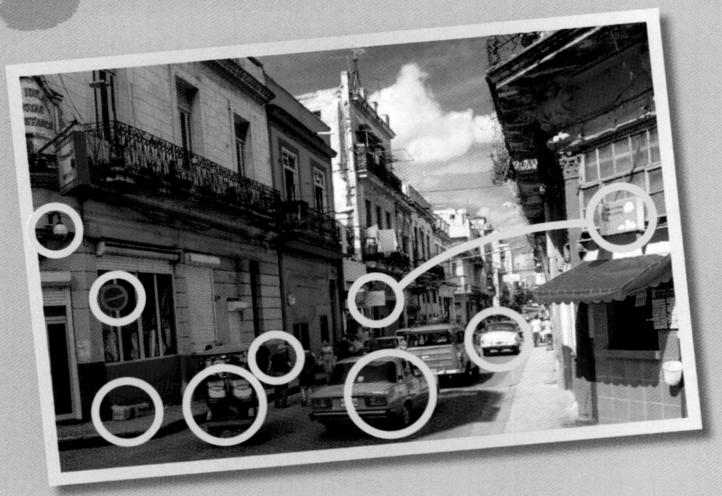

17 AMSTERDAM

19 DUBLIN

A = 7 B = 2
C = 3 D = 6

20 BRUSSELS

23 VIENNA

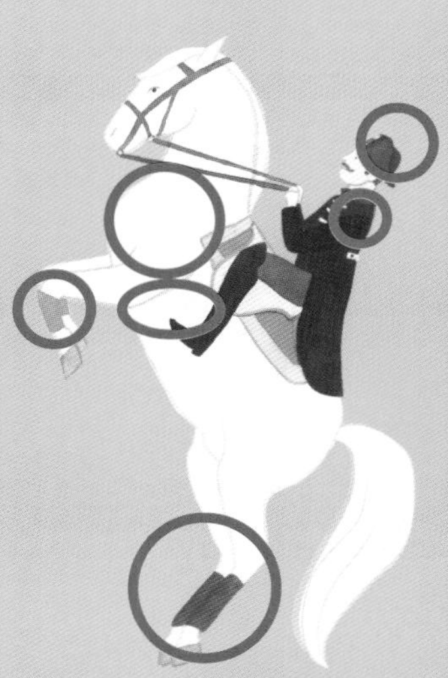

23 ATHENS

There are 153 books.

24 MADRID

There are 33 fish.

26 TIMBUKTU

Trail 1 leads to termite mound A.
Trail 2 leads to termite mound B.
Trail 3 leads to termite mound C.

32 JERUSALEM

33 DUBAI

35 MUMBAI

36 BĚIJĪNG

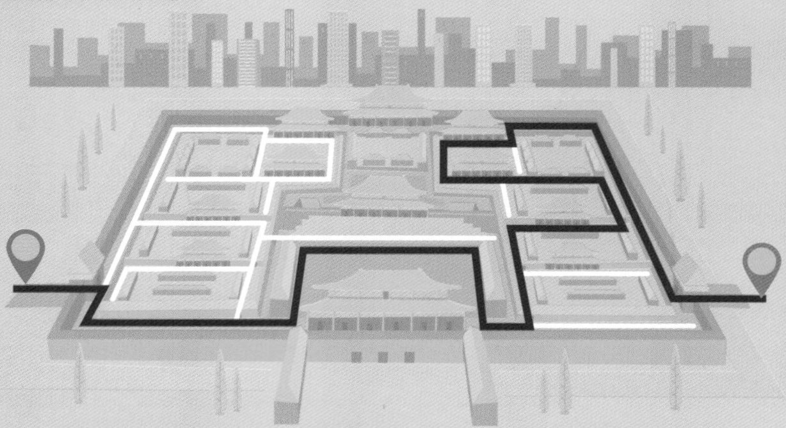

37 CHÉNGDŪ

38 BANGKOK

39 MANILA

40 TOKYO

There are 21 passengers.

ACKNOWLEDGEMENTS

Editorial and Design by Tall Tree Ltd

Authors: Heather Carswell, Bridget Gleeson, Patrick Kinsella, Hugh McNaughtan, Nicola Williams, Karla Zimmerman, Emma Marriott
Illustrators: Livi Gosling and Tom Woolley
Publishing Director: Piers Pickard
Publisher: Hanna Otero
Art Director: Andy Mansfield
Commissioning Editor: Joe Fullman
Print Production: Lisa Ford

Published in June 2019 by Lonely Planet Global Ltd

CRN: 554153
ISBN: 978 1 78868 476 7

www.lonelyplanetkids.com

Printed in Malaysia
10 9 8 7 6 5 4 3 2 1

STAY IN TOUCH
lonelyplanet.com/contact

Lonely Planet Offices

AUSTRALIA The Malt Store, Level 3, 551 Swanston St, Carlton, Victoria 3053 T: 03 8379 8000
IRELAND Digital Depot, Roe Lane (off Thomas St), Digital Hub, Dublin 8, D08 TCV4
UK 240 Blackfriars Rd, London SE1 8NW T: 020 3771 5100
USA 124 Linden St, Oakland, CA 94607 T: 510 250 6400

FSC www.fsc.org MIX Paper from responsible sources FSC™ C021741

Paper in this book is certified against the Forest Stewardship Council™ standards. FSC™ promotes environmentally responsible, socially beneficial and economically viable management of the world's forests.

PHOTOGRAPHY CREDITS

Key l=left, r=right, t=top, tl=top left, tc=top centre, tr=top right, c=centre, cl=centre left, cr=centre right, b=bottom, bl=bottom left, bc=bottom centre, br=bottom right.

Alamy
p13 frans lemmens

Getty Images
p11 (t) Peter Macdiarmid p20 (l) Heidi Coppock-Beard p31 (t) Bernd Siering (b) Thomas Imo

Shutterstock
p10 (t) Kamira p20 (br) Orapin Joyphuem p27 (tr) Valentin Valkov p28 (tl) Birute Vijeikiene p32 (t) ChameleonsEye p38 (t) nimon p43 (cl) Neale Cousland

ILLUSTRATION CREDITS

Shutterstock
p5 Jane Mori p16 (b) ShustrikS p25 (t) Afishka p 6 (b) JPL Designs p37 (t) Ecaterina Sciuchina

All other illustrations by Livi Gosling and Tom Woolley

p.6-7
p.8-9
MGM
p.10
p.12

p.14-15

p.17

p.18-19

p.21
p.22
p.24-25
p.28-29

p.26

p.30

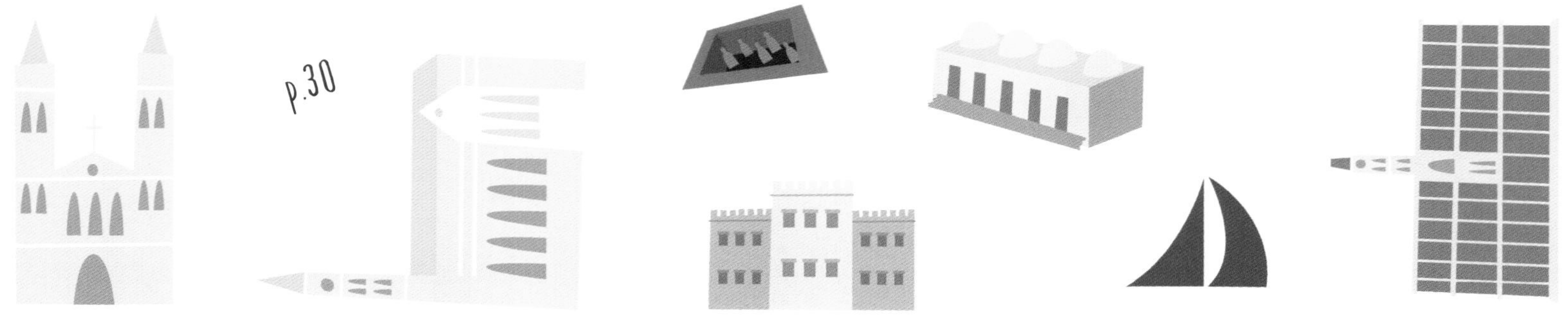

p.32-33

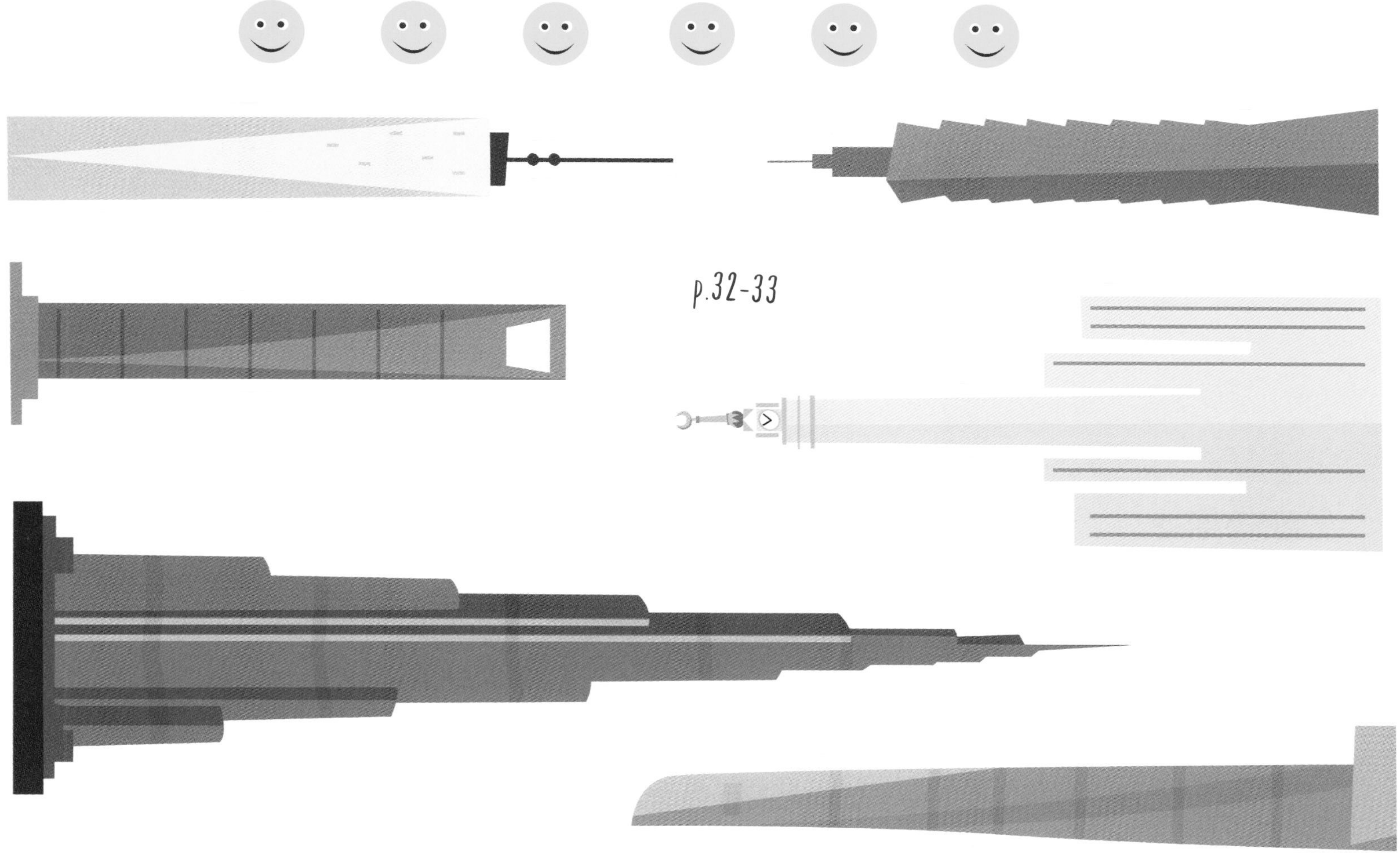

p.34

p.37

p.38

p.34-35

p.40-41

p.44-45

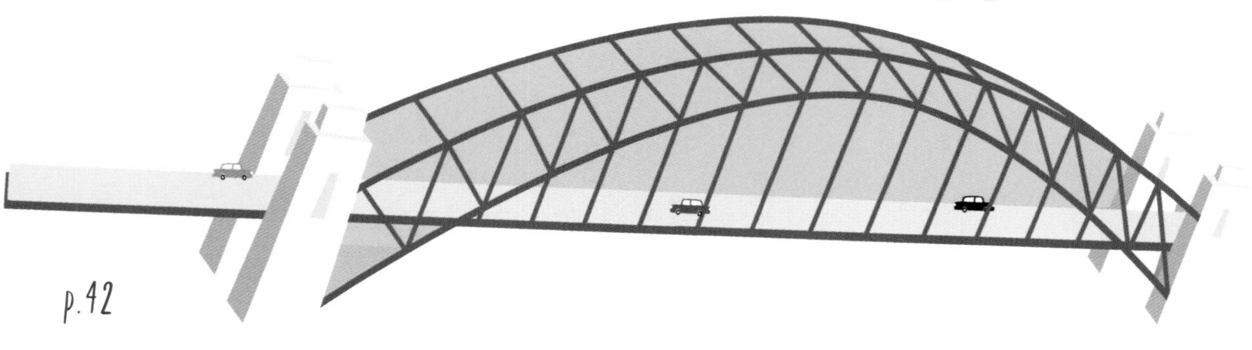

p.42